She's
Still
Here

To my soul tribe,
with Love,
Mehrnaz

She's Still Here

Published in Canada by MFC Publications

Book Cover and Layout by Galley Creative Co.

ISBN 978-1-7381490-0-1 (Bound)
ISBN 978-1-7381490-1-8 (ePub)

She's Still Here

Healing Short Stories *for* Women

MEHRNAZ MASSOUDI

For Laila and Roya—loving
you was my kick ass guru to
learn the true meaning of
unconditional love.

Contents

I'm Not Taking This With Me 9

Cara's Flower Garden 25

Om 37

Grateful-for-Liam Cards 61

Malak the Angel 79

Masturbating in a Buddhist Monastery 97

She's Still Here 119

Kenzie's Mermaids 143

Gramma Ji 159

Acknowledgments 177

About the Author 179

I'm Not Taking This With Me

I AM SITTING in the waiting room to get a blood test. I had my first chemo three weeks ago. This afternoon I'm going for my second treatment. Before they give me my dose, they need a blood test to make sure my white cell count is high enough. If it is too low, they will reschedule. I hope my count will be good.

I just can't believe that my life has taken such a turn that all I'm wishing for is my blood count to be right, so I can have a cancer treatment today!

My friend Tara took the day off work to drive me to the clinic and back. My friends organized between them who will take me and who will stay with me the day after. After my first treatment, I was in bed all the next day, feeling like I had the flu—no vomiting, just crazy nauseous, and exhausted. I was grateful that one of my friends was there to take care of me.

There are at least ten people ahead of me in the lab. We all take a number and each time the lab technician calls one out, we glance down at ours. Is everyone as nervous as me?

There is an old woman, maybe in her eighties, speaking loudly to a woman sitting next to her. I stare at my cellphone, but am too nervous to pay attention to anything. I keep scrolling on my phone and listening to the lady. I hear her say, "Well dear, at least it's not cancer!"

I'm thirty-eight, I'm not married, I don't have kids, and I have stage four breast cancer. What have I got for an "at least it's not..." line?

Mark couldn't take it any longer. We had only been living together for two years when I got the breast cancer diagnosis.

It all started with a bad cold that lasted for weeks and then the coughing wouldn't stop. It was after the chest X-ray that I got the call from my doctor's office. They'd found nodules on my lungs and more tests were ordered. After two weeks of testing, I was diagnosed with advanced breast cancer.

Mark was amazing through all the chemo treatments and surgeries, but after two years as my main caregiver, he emotionally collapsed. It hurt so much when he left, but most of the time I was so numb from the painkillers that everything seemed vague. I don't remember our last words.

I don't remember if we hugged each other the day he left.

One night shortly after he left, I sat up in bed disoriented. I looked around my room trying to figure out where I was. Was I dreaming or awake?

I must have been hallucinating on the painkillers.

I lay back down and dreamed I was covered with tumours, with lumps sticking out of my head, my throat, and all over my body. I was in so much pain. Then I felt I was floating on a clear blue ocean. I'd never seen anything like it—the water gently rocked me back and forth. But when I moved my hands through it there were no water drops—only droplets of light.

I held the shimmering droplets in my hands and poured them over my head. I felt them tumble over me and go right through me. Suddenly there was no pain, and I was floating effortlessly on the sapphire sea.

"I'm not sure if this was a dream," I told Tara. I'm taking so many pills, maybe I was just hallucinating." She was always fascinated by my dreams.

"Melissa," she said, "you need to find out what that dream means. I'll take you to see a shaman. It will be a present from me. You need to know what it means."

Since my diagnosis I dreaded going to bed at night. Everything hurt more in the dark, but after my dream I look forward to sleeping. If I can just have one more dream like that: no pain, no lumps, only magical drops of light... floating on the calm ocean... feeling the sensation of buoyancy...

I was apprehensive about seeing a shaman. Would she judge me for taking so many pills and choosing to do chemo? Don't shamans only believe in natural remedies? Would she think that I was hallucinating because of the pills?

The room is smoky with burning sage. Before the shaman says a word she walks around and moves the air with a fan made of feathers. I learn later they are eagle feathers. The room is beautiful, draped with tapestries from around the world and with brightly coloured, comfortable-looking chairs. On the floor is a spectacular Persian rug. I was expecting a shaman's room to be darker, a weird, ghostly space.

Her name is Mayra. Her maternal grandparents moved from Ireland to Canada.

"My great-great-grandmother was among the women burned in Ireland for the crime of witchcraft," Mayra says. Her first shamanic teacher was in Ireland.

"And I've had the honour of learning from Indigenous shamans here in Canada," she says.

I take a seat and she tells me to put my feet up on a turquoise Moroccan poof. After a short conversation she plays a rhythmic pattern on a native-looking drum and asks me to close my eyes. My body begins gently vibrating with the beat of her drumming. Then she comes in close and shakes rattles made from gourds over me and says in a calm, quiet voice, "Your spirit animal is Eagle." Then she continues shaking the rattles.

'There is an energy in your womb that tells me you have suffered from sexual abuse. Do I have your permission to work on it?"

"Yes," I manage to say, trying to hold back my tears.

She lights some incense with a distinctive smell and creates more sounds close to my body—small clicking noises and then an almost inaudible song. I open my eyes a crack and watch her wave her hand in a circular rotation over my womb.

"Open your eyes when you're ready."

I sit and cry. She gently holds my hand.

I knew that I should've forgiven him for sexually abusing me, but I couldn't.

I'd read everything about forgiveness and the message is always the same: "When we don't forgive, the hatred makes us sick."

But I couldn't forgive him.

And then I hear Mayra saying, "In this lifetime, the only person you must forgive is you." She looks deep into my eyes and holds my hand.

I feel like I've been zapped with something. The way she looks at me—every word she says has electrical power, cutting right through me like a laser to my heart. All these years, I had tried to forgive him and failed.

What I really wanted was to see him suffer. I wished him a brutal death. Many times, I dreamed of killing him myself. The more I thought of forgiving him, the more agitated I became.

Mayra's words are so powerful and yet kind and gentle. "The only person you must forgive is you."

Mom and Dad have been my pillars. After using all my sick days from work, my disability insurance kicked in, but it wasn't enough—especially after Mark left and I had to pay the full rent myself. Now Mom and Dad pay half and they keep offering to help more. "If you need anything extra, please just ask."

They buy most of my groceries. I have no energy for grocery shopping, anyway. Mom reads every article about fighting cancer. There are so many stories about non-organic foods poisoning us. Why the fuck doesn't our government make organic food more affordable? They could save billions in health care and have a stronger nation.

I don't want to ask Mom and Dad to pay for anything else. I feel bad enough about them paying for so much already. But after my first visit with Mayra I feel she can help me "surrender to the next realm": whatever the fuck that means. I really need to "not take this with me"—all the hatred and anger I'm carrying for "him," my rapist! I ask Mom to pay for one more visit with Mayra.

I ask Mayra about my dream.

"The tumours in your dream represent the anger, resentment, blame, guilt, and other emotions that you've been holding onto—the stories that you have been repeating all your life. The stories of 'if.'"

Yep, the stories of "if" have been playing in my head since that night!

If I had told the police, then maybe he would not have sexually assaulted that little two-year-old girl.

Mayra says, "In your dream you experienced your true essence, which is that we are one with the water and the light. There is no separation between you, water, and light. In that state there is no story to tell—it's all love.

"The state that you felt in your dream, 'swimming effortlessly,' is the state we are born in and it's the same state we experience when we die."

"So, does this dream mean that I'm dying?," I ask her. "I mean, I know I'm dying, but somehow, I'm hoping that I won't die just yet. After every test I hope that my oncologist will tell me that the cancer is gone. But the days when the pain is hard to bear, I do want to die!"

Mayra nods in understanding. "In your dream, you felt and saw the true meaning of life. Once we swim to the core there is nothing but love, peace, and surrender. That's why you didn't feel the pain anymore. Are you dying? I can't answer that."

She pauses and reflects.

"Have you heard of Anita Moorjani? She was in the end stages of cancer and had slipped into a coma. Her doctors left her to die. She had a near-death experience and, when she came back to life, she was miraculously healed. This all happened in the hospital. It's documented. I recommend you read her book *Dying to Be Me.*"

I downloaded Moorjani's audiobook and listened to it between the comatose and awake stages of my day. The painkiller dosage was so high that when I took them, I became completely unconscious. Anita Moorjani's miraculous healing was inspiring and so was her message of "self-love and self-acceptance".

What will I do if I am given one more chance? What do I want to do with the remaining days of my life? How do I forgive myself?

I started a blog called *I'm Not Taking This With Me,* and the words came tumbling out of me in a way I had never experienced before.

"Fuck you, cancer! I'm not letting you take me now. I have a job to finish."

I can't stop writing. My pain is severe and real, but I have to stay awake to write and the painkillers put me to sleep. No one knows how much cancer hurts except those who have gone through it. I tolerate the pain and write until it's intolerable and then I take the drugs.

MAY 10, 2023

I was sixteen and sleeping over at a friend's house after a party. When we got back to her house, she passed out. But the alcohol I drank kept me awake, so I went to the kitchen for a drink of water. Her dad was there drinking whisky. He offered me one, but I declined. Then he offered me beer. I was already drunk, but I drank more. He was charming and funny and I laughed at his jokes. Then he asked me to go down to their family room in the basement. I followed him. He closed the door and attacked me.

I blame myself for getting drunk with him, for going to the basement. I should have known. I blame myself.

I shared that story with my followers. I told them where I lived, which school I'd gone to and what year I was born. But what I couldn't tell them was his name, his address, or his daughter's name, or I could be charged with making a false accusation! For harassment. For defamation of character.

I didn't report him to the police.

I'd gone to my family physician, but my rapist didn't ejaculate inside me so there was no evidence.

MAY 15, 2023

A few years later, I heard that his wife closed her home-based daycare business. She claimed that she developed carpal tunnel in her wrists and was no longer able to operate her daycare. But the story I heard was that a two-year-old girl had been sexually assaulted and her daycare centre was under investigation. No one was charged.

MAY 30, 2023

To the parents of the two-year-old girl, and that little girl herself, please forgive me for not coming forward. I told my parents, but they thought that no one would believe me. And when I heard about the little girl I wanted to go to the police, but my parents discouraged me.

"Honey, this news has triggered you again," they said. You should go see your therapist."

I knew they meant well, but how is that helping anyone? I'm so sorry. Please forgive me, little girl who is now a young woman.

JUNE 4, 2023

My dear readers, you have no idea how much, after all these years, I wish I could tell you his name.

Thank you, the amazing guy who asked me to private message his identity so you and your friends could go "beat the shit out of him." Thank you! I love you and I love your friends. You guys rock!

But in these last days of my life, I don't want him to be beaten up. All I want is to share my message with those who were victimized by him and stop him from hurting anyone else.

And I want to stop blaming myself.

For years, I thought it was my fault. Today I know it wasn't. He's a sick man and is probably still hurting other innocent girls and women. He's a grandfather now and I worry that his grandchildren are in danger. My sincere gratitude for your empathy—for feeling my pain. If you want to do something to help, please share my blog with your friends. LOVE YOU.

JUNE 8, 2023

Today, the pain is really bad again. Thank you for sending me love and healing energy. I can't write much. I have to take extra painkillers and hope it goes away so I can sleep.

JUNE 10, 2023

My response to your comment: Yes, I eventually did contact the police and gave them his name when I heard about the two-year-old girl. A fabulous detective worked with me, but she said that the file was closed and she could not reopen the case or forward my information to the parents of the two-year-old girl.

Thank you for encouraging me to "keep writing your blog—it might get to the parents of the girl." I will. The detective encouraged me, too.

Please forgive me. Thank you. I love you.

JUNE 12, 2023

Oh, wow, I got a comment from someone in Hawaii.

Thank you for your response! Yes, I know that what I am doing is Ho'oponopono, the Hawaiian practice of reconciliation and forgiveness. I'm also doing Ho'oponopono for me. It's time to love and forgive myself. "Thank you. I'm sorry. Please forgive me. I love you."

JUNE 14, 2023

I'm so sorry that you experienced the same horrible thing as me. You are the first reader to come forward, but I know his list of victims doesn't end with you and me. There must be many of us around the same age as his daughter. I'm so sorry but I can't meet you tomorrow. As you know I'm in a lot of pain and spend most of my time in bed and I can't drive while taking drugs. But a friend is organizing a meeting in two weeks, and we believe there will be more women coming forward. Don't worry, I will not share your name in my blog.

I will PM you the date and the place. I'm so sorry for what you've endured. Sending hugs, Melissa.

JUNE 28, 2023

Mom, I know I was told that my cancer is in the last stage, but neither the doctor nor anyone else can tell me how long I have to live. What I would like is for you to think of me as healthy. When you're walking down the hallway of my building toward my apartment door, please don't think of me as dying. I need you to envision me living—living today, tomorrow, and the next day. I know that over the past two years I haven't been able to think about anything but dying, but from today on I ask that you and anyone else coming into my space bring me a breeze, a whisper, a prayer for me to be living fully in this moment… and the next… and the next.

When I was diagnosed with cancer, I read everything about starving the cancer with a plant-based, low-sugar diet. Mom and I found easy, vegan, and almost-sugar-free recipes. Now I see that my quick reaction to change my diet was a fight-or-flight response. I wasn't operating from a place of love and compassion. I was being driven by my fear.

Thinking back on that transformational dream and Mayra's interpretation of it, I can now sense and taste the essence of her message about Love and Fear.

I keep saying I'm not going to ask anything more from my parents and then, Mom, one more thing. Or two or three things. Ha.

"Mom, could you pick up some of my favourite coffee beans? And on Valentine's Day, I would really love it if you could bring me a few of my favourite chocolates. Oh, and a box of mangoes from that East Indian store we like, please, Mom, and a big watermelon."

I have been avoiding eating fruits high in sugar. Now that I'm not eating out of fear—I'm craving mango and watermelon, and, ooh, drinking coffee with a piece of chocolate in my mouth, melting ever so slowly and blending on my tongue into the liquid.

In the midst of pain… suffering… fear of dying… I am madly craving living… desiring the sweet orange mango… the red juicy watermelon…

Craving, with all my essence, moments of living.

When I die, if an angel or anyone else in the other realm asks me to describe my precious memory from this lifetime, this is what I'll say: my life was as sweetly intoxicating as the first taste of chocolate on my tongue with my eyes closed as the creamy, dark, ambrosia slowly melts through my mouth… the first bite of a slice of a perfectly ripe, crispy, juicy watermelon, the crunch in my ears, the refreshing sweetness on my tongue… waking up to the smell of coffee in the morning. So many sweet memories.

And especially this one: the sound of the key going into the lock, a gentle knocking, and my mother's voice saying, "Melissa, darling. It's me, Mom," as she walks in like an angel to hold me, to help me.

I was in that state between sleeping and waking when speaking to the angel about my sweet memories from this life. When I opened my eyes, Mom was in the kitchen doing my dishes.

"Mom, I'm not giving up, but I'm also not fighting it anymore. I want to be here, but what I want the most is to feel the love. I fucking hate the thought of saying goodbye to you, Mom."

I sobbed while she held me.

Dad is barbecuing free-range organic chicken for my fortieth birthday. He was so proud that he found it on sale. Before my diagnosis, he was a straight up meat-and-potatoes guy and a bargain shopper. He didn't care how animals were raised or treated—the cheaper the better.

People ask me if I follow a special diet now that I have cancer, if I'm vegan, vegetarian, lacto-vegetarian, or ovo-lacto vegetarian? I am not. I'm not a flexitarian either. If I had to call how I am eating, I would say that I am choosing to eat compassionately.

I would like fewer animals to be killed for the purpose of feeding me.

Mom and Dad didn't think I would live to celebrate my fortieth birthday so this is a very special celebration. Dad loves to barbecue and is making all the food today. Tara, Grandma, and my brother Jacob are here. I dislike store-bought veggie burgers and Mom offered to make me a homemade patty. But she's been cooking and juicing and making smoothies for me every day, so I didn't want her to have to prepare anything today.

Today—on my fortieth birthday—I will eat pasture-raised chicken to make my dad happy and save myself from a store-bought veggie burger that tastes like cardboard!

When I was thirty-eight, my oncologist said I might have three to six months to live.

Today, I'm not just celebrating the big "four-zero." I'm celebrating the miracle of still being here.

A week ago, I met with the doctor to go over the tests. I cannot describe the fear I was feeling; there are no words. My body was so cold and frozen with fear that I could not let a drop of light in. With a shaky voice I said, "Doc, please remember, just the diagnosis, no prognosis!"

The tests indicated that the tumours were growing at a slower rate. Not shrinking in size, but not growing as fast. When the chemo treatments were terminated last year—because it wasn't working, it wasn't killing the cancer cells, or shrinking the tumours—I was told that I would need to start thinking about moving to a hospice. I went with Mom and Dad to have a look. The hospice was a beautiful and peaceful place. But no matter how nice they make it, it's still a place to go to die. I wasn't ready yet.

Even though I hated the chemo treatments, I was afraid when they were terminated. I *believed* that it was working, killing the cancer cells and destroying the tumours. And now the thought of the cancer maybe growing at a faster rate without anything stopping or slowing it down was horrifying. Even if chemo gave me a false security, it was something.

"Well, continue doing whatever you're doing," the oncologist said.

I couldn't hold back my tears. Although the cancerous tumours were still slowly growing this was the best news I'd had in a long time. The doc gave me a hug as I was leaving and said, "I don't believe in saying things like 'sending you love and light' or 'I'll pray for you,' but I will say, 'may the force be with you always.'"

AUGUST 1, 2023

My dear readers, now there are five other women who have come forward. All of us were sexually assaulted by the same man. After many meetings, we have collectively decided to bring this man to justice. Only two women among us reported their cases to the police, but he was not charged because there was no evidence.

> *In every case he didn't discharge inside his victim.*
>
> *I reported it to my family physician a few days after the incident. Many of us have told our stories to therapists for many years. We are now trying to locate these therapists. Some have retired, moved, or passed on. We are now searching for a compassionate lawyer. All we want is to prevent him from hurting another innocent child or woman. I now know that I'm not taking this with me when I die.*

Every morning I close my eyes and visualize the light entering every cell in my body. I hear Mayra's words from our last session resonating through my body and all around me: "You have awakened your inner healer. Now and for the rest of your journey all you need to do is trust it. Expect nothing and be open to everything."

Cara's Flower Garden

TOMORROW IS YOUR birthday.

It's been eight months since you've been gone.

I wasted your last birthday, filled it with fear about you drinking with your friends. All my worrying for nothing because you still managed to get someone to buy you drinks. You said, "Mom! I'm seventeen! Everyone drinks on their seventeenth birthday!"

We fought. And then I wasted the next day fuming in silence because you were hungover.

Most of last year—the last year I had you—we fought.

My friends tell me not to blame myself. They say, "Alicia, let go of the dark thoughts. Only think of the good times you shared."

How can they possibly know this ache in my heart? All I can think about are the lost moments. The wasted opportunities for joy with my daughter.

I used to get so angry when the phone rang and the school's recorded message would say you'd skipped school that day. I was afraid that you were into drugs and drinking. You quit taking piano lessons and you played so well. I lived in fear that you would become a drug addict or an alcoholic like your grandmother.

Fear is my biggest enemy. Fear robbed me of just being with you and enjoying every precious second. Tomorrow is your birthday and all I can think of is ending my life so I won't have to spend your birthday without you.

But I'm not brave enough to kill myself.

Instead, I took sleeping pills. On the morning of your birthday, Dad brought me coffee in bed. You have his eyes and when I looked into them, I just sobbed. He held me. He is suffering, too.

You have his eyes... his smoky brown eyes... You have my sandy blond wavy hair... You have—I'm still thinking of you in the present... One moment you are here: you are the centre of my universe and then in one second my universe crumbles and you are not here anymore. And just like that you've become the past tense.

A part of me knows that I need to stay here for Adam. He was such a good big brother to you—he misses his little sister.

From the moment we got the call about the crash I became paralyzed... paralyzed inside. My body moves but nothing inside me moves.

"Adam sent a text for Cara's birthday. Have you read it?" Paul says.

I just look at him and have a sip of coffee. I can't talk. Not a word.

"Is there anything I can do for you, honey? You've been in bed for two days."

"Yes, you can help me die. Please..." and I sobbed some more.

Kelly says, "Alicia, please get out of bed and come into the kitchen and eat something. I bought daffodil bulbs for the garden. Let's plant them for Cara." Aunt Kelly still has her green thumb.

I sit on the patio and watch your aunt Kelly plant daffodils and talk to you like you are sitting next to her the whole time.

Your friend Jessica texted and asked to come see me today. I managed to get out of bed and make your favourite cookies.

I'm trying to be strong in front of Jessica. She misses you. She's excited about graduation, but at the same time, she's so sad that you won't be there. She talked about your graduation dreams and how the two of you planned to go to the same university. And then she showed me a locket with a picture of you. She said she bought it on your birthday, and then she pressed it to her heart. She choked out she couldn't imagine going through graduation without you.

Poor sweet Jessica, suffering the loss of you, Cara, her best friend, at such a young age.

"Alicia," Kelly says, "come out and see the daffodil shoots. They're so green. Remember how Cara loved to water the flowerpots on my balcony when she was little? She gave them names and always wanted to have a tea party out there with the flowers. She would pour tea into a spoon and then drizzled it around each flower."

"She loved you, Kelly. While I was busy working and planning her future, you were with her in the moment and made precious memories."

"Oh, come on, Sis," Kelly says, "You were the responsible one. And I'm so grateful for that. You were the one who paid for my plane tickets home from Mexico, and another time from India when I was so broke. You working made it possible for me to have time with Cara.

"One of my favourite memories of us was the time you rented that cabin on the lake for the kids and me. Mom and Dad wouldn't even trust me to house-sit for them because I drank and smoked weed, but you trusted me with Cara and Adam. I'll cherish that memory for the rest of my life."

I really hate it when friends suggest therapy or a support group and say, "Alicia, you have to move on. Think about Paul and Adam. Cara would want you to be happy."

All that does is make me want to knock myself out with more sleeping pills. The only thing I look forward to is Kelly's company. She comes twice a week and makes me tea. I sit on the patio and watch her gardening. The day the daffodils bloomed, she danced around the flowers with tears streaming down her face.

Paul doesn't understand what her gardening means to me. To us.

He's worried that she will stop coming around and then he'll have to hire a landscaper to replace all the grass she's dug up.

He doesn't see that the only time I sit on the patio is when my sister is gardening.

"I'm going to Jessica's graduation," Kelly says, "I know that's what Cara wants me to do. I'll bring Jessica a beautiful bouquet of flowers. She really misses Cara and I think it would comfort her."

"Oh Kelly, you are so courageous! How can you sit through that ceremony?"

"I don't know. I just know I want to be there. I asked Jessica's mom if she would keep an eye on me and call me an Uber if I lose it. I don't care if people see me crying, Alicia. I would hope they would be more concerned if I didn't cry."

"I don't know how you can do it. I know you are hurting, too, but you keep showing up for Adam, Paul and me, and now Jessica."

"I choose to meet the pain with love. I would give anything to hold my sweet little niece one more time. I focus on the feeling of love I have for her. When I'm in the garden, I feel her... I feel Cara's presence."

"I don't feel anything. I'm frozen inside. Do you think she's still mad at me for fighting with her so much? Is that why I don't feel her?"

"Maybe you can't feel Cara because you are mad at yourself, beating yourself up for the times you fought with her. Blaming yourself. I think if you tried remembering all the good things, all the right choices you made, how deeply you cared about her, things would change.

"Alicia, you loved her with all your heart. Think about that and you'll be able to feel her."

"Oh Kelly, I wish I had what you have. You've always had it—even when you were a kid, the way you sat in the garden and watched a butterfly, a ladybug...

"You sat in the garden so quietly that birds trusted you and sat close to you as they were pecking in the grass."

Leslie emailed. She said it took her a while to gain the courage to write. She misses me at tennis. She wants me to come play. She wants to know how she can help.

I wrote her back and told her that my only exercise is watching my sister garden, that I really appreciated the thought and would love to meet for tea, but not just yet. She replied that she would write in a month and invite me for tea again and that she wishes there were something she could do.

I wish there were something she could do.

"I remember the daffodils in India," Kelly says. "They were so fragrant. These don't have that same intensity, but they are still beautiful. Alicia, come look at this."

"I don't feel like walking."

"Okay. I'll pick it and bring it to you… you lazy bum."

"No, don't pick any, please. I love looking at them from my bedroom window. I want them all to be there."

"It's just… I can't express it… but when I bring my face to one of these blossoms… I get a sense… that we are all connected. Like how can I say it? Umm, it feels like our souls are not separate entities… There is nothing separating us. The separation is just a thought. "

I get up from bed and walk to the garden with Kelly. She lays down on the grass and cries. I sit next to her and put her head on my lap. I stare at the daffodil, trying to sense what Kelly senses.

Adam is home for summer break. He wants Kelly and her wife, Lindsey, to come for lunch. Lindsey hasn't been in the house since the celebration of life. She can't bear to be in the house without Cara. Adam does the dishes, Kelly heads into the garden and Lindsey and I sit in awkward silence on the porch.

"I'm so glad Kelly created this garden in your yard. It's helping her to heal. She's done a bunch of pots on our balcony, too. It's her way of dealing with..." Lindsey pauses. She's trying to hold her tears back.

"Yeah, it is her way... She keeps asking to take out more grass."

"I can imagine how that's going."

"Yep... Paul doesn't like to spend money and as we know well, he's never liked Kelly. I remember when the two of you moved in together. He didn't want the kids to come to your place and, of course, my mom supported his idea."

"I'm so glad you stood up to him, Alicia. Being around Cara and Adam has been one of the most precious gifts in our lives."

"Cara was the one who blew your cover, Lindsey. She told Mom and Dad that Auntie Kelly was living with another woman. I told them you were just roommates. And Cara said, "No, Mom. Aunt Kelly and Aunt Lindsey are married now. I married them in the rose garden."

We both can't talk. I just have to let the tears pour. Cara, how can I hold them back when I'm thinking of how excited you were marrying your aunts?

"It was Cara's idea," Lindsey says "She made Kelly and me wear white shirts and she put makeup on me and said I was the most beautiful bride. Alicia, I should have come sooner, but I..."

Cara, your Aunt Lindsey can't finish her sentence. She is crying and, somehow, I feel the strength to soothe her. Although I am still frozen inside—it is such a strange feeling—it is like watching myself emerge from my frozen self and take the steps to hold Lindsey.

There is two of me: one who is stuck and frozen, and the other one is fluid and light.

"Paul, do you remember when you didn't want the kids to sleep over at my sister's because you were afraid that they would see inappropriate things because she's gay?

"Do you know that Lindsey has been sending cookies to Adam at college?

"Listen very carefully to what I am about to ask because your answer will determine whether or not we continue to live together. Kelly would like to turn the front lawn into a flower garden for Cara. Could you please let Kelly know what you think of that idea?"

"I don't know what you said to Paul. We're gonna dig this up fast before he changes his mind."

Kelly and her friends are over and are digging up the grass.

Adam offers to shop and makes lunch for the crew. I make potato salad and we have burgers and beers. This is the first time in a long time that I feel at ease around people.

This morning, I get up early to water the flowers. Kelly is adamant about watering before the sun comes up. She is surprised to find me in the garden. I tell her that I had a dream that I was holding you and walking through a garden of flowers. You were just a baby, but you kept leaning out to touch the beautiful blossoms. You looked so happy, Cara.

Ever since you left, Cara, this heavy mass of darkness has sat on my heart. But now, after my dream of you in the flower garden, I feel a small flickering light.

Jessica and a couple more of your friends have an amazing idea. They want to take a video of the garden and post it on social media. I go to the office and make a sign: "Cara's Flower Garden."

I feel exhausted after making the sign and stay in bed for the rest of the day. Jessica asks me to be in the video, but I want Kelly to be in it—it's her idea, her way of coping with your loss.

After everyone leaves, we sit in your garden with our tea. I use my spoon and drizzle tea around the flowers near me.

Aunt Kelly says, "She's not gone, is she? She's still here, right here." She points at your garden.

Your video has gone viral, overnight! And now your kind aunt Kelly has offered her help as a memorial garden creator to other parents who've lost their kids.

"Kelly, I am inviting Mom to come over and see the garden. Let her be proud of you for once. Will you come?"

"Nope. Mom still blames me for getting Cara into drinking and weed. If she and Paul have one thing in common, it's blaming me for everything they didn't approve of. Remember when she scolded me for bringing Adam an apron from Mexico?

"He was so happy wearing it baking cookies. I'm sure she thought he would turn gay if he baked instead of playing hockey. He was only ten, for fuck sake."

I'm taking a lower dose of sleeping pills. I don't want to feel dopey in the mornings. I get up early to water the flowers. Kelly still does the dirty work, weeding and keeping everything beautiful. Your garden video has gotten so much attention. People from all over are posting about their lost loved ones and offering funds for future projects. Kelly's dream of being of service to others has come true. Because of you.

I know it's a cliché, but it's so true — "it's only when you are in the darkness that you see the light."

"So, Alicia, who exactly is Luke? He said he works with you. Why are you clearing your throat? Are you nervous?"

"Oh, stop it. You have these crazy theories and you beam when you think you're right."

Kelly likes to tease me about Luke. He's been kind to me. Luke looked after his wife while she fought cancer for five years. He is a good man. He's a colleague of mine.

It has been a long time since I have felt any passion for your father. Ever since I found out about his affair. You didn't know about this. I was waiting for you to graduate, then I was leaving him. He's the one who started cheating on me, but he is jealous of my friendship with Luke.

After I water the flowers in the mornings, I make myself tea and go straight to my desk to read the messages from Cara's Flower Garden's followers. Kelly is busy building another garden for a family who lost their twelve-year-old daughter to cancer. I answer the messages and write a blog. The blog is inspired by messages we've been receiving from people around the world who also lost a loved one.

"I've lost my grandson to a drug overdose. He was my life."

"I lost my baby—Xander was only one year old. It makes me so angry when people say that Xander is in a better place now. My husband and I so loved him. He was happy here."

Hearing their stories and writing them back has become my purpose. Another gift from you, Cara.

"Sis," Kelly says, idly checking her dirty fingernails, "guess who asked me out for a drink last night."

"Tell."

"Luke!"

"Oh, no! You didn't!"

"Don't get ahead of yourself. It was innocent. He offered to design chairs for the flower garden. I told him that he wasn't going to use Cara's Flower Garden for advertising his firm. He said that wasn't what he had in mind."

"Did you get drunk? Because I don't trust you when you drink, Kelly."

"Haha, thanks, Sis! No, I didn't get drunk. We had a few drinks and I told him not to ask you out for another year. That you were waiting to leave Paul after Cara graduated and now you're waiting for Adam to cope with Cara's loss before you introduce another stress into his life."

"Kelly, fuck! How dare you!"

I start pounding on my little sister's arm. She manages to get a hold of my hands so I kick her. We laugh so hard. It has been a long time since we gave each other a good beating or had such a deep belly laugh. Teasing and laughing like when we were little.

Cara, do you see me? This is your mom when she isn't carrying the weight of the world on her back. Not taking responsibility for everyone and everything or looking for approval from her husband or her friends or her mother. She is wild… your mom… and you were just like her.

We sit in the garden drinking wine. Adam comes home from work and we open another bottle.

Today, a golden-orange butterfly sits on a flower in your garden. It flies away so gently. I keep watching it as it flies, growing smaller and smaller until I can't see it anymore. I am starting to feel the same way about you—just because I can't see you doesn't mean that you're not here.

I love you forever.

Mom's beautiful daffodil, peony, dahlia, rose…

Om

MY HEART IS beating so fast. I'm shaking. I hope these nightmares of seeing Matt having sex with other women stop soon.

One Saturday morning when we were having coffee, Matt said, "I've been soul-searching lately and I feel like I need to be alone. Ash, I love you, but you know that we've been growing apart."

We fought like any other couple I knew. He had said more than once that he wasn't happy, but then we would distract ourselves with travelling to Europe, Hawaii, and South America. We got along well when we travelled, but after we got back into our daily lives, the fights would start again.

"Matt, is it my body? I know I've put on weight, but I was planning to hire a trainer and lose it."

"Oh, hon, you've always been on the heavy side of the scale, even when we met. It's not your body, Ash."

"I know, but I've never been this heavy before. I can do it, Matt, I will lose weight. Don't leave me, Matt." I was begging him.

After twelve years together, Matt packed and left.

He said he had rented a room from a guy at work, but I found out he had moved in with another woman. They'd been dating for over a year.

It was when I ran into Matt and his girlfriend that I understood what Matt meant when he said, "you've always been on the heavy side of the scale." She was stunning with a perfect, thin, athletic body. I felt like a whale next to her. What he really meant was "you could never have her body."

After months of doing nothing but going to work, coming home, watching Netflix, and eating, I finally decided to join a gym. I hate gyms. I always feel I'm being judged when I walk in the door, as though the people at the desk are thinking, "It's about time."

I had gained more weight since Matt left and I felt desperate to lose it. After two months of dieting and going to the gym a few times a week, I lost less than ten pounds. I don't know who came up with the statement, "The first twenty pounds come off easily," but that wasn't my experience. Maybe there is something wrong with my thyroid? Weight was coming off so slowly, I was killing myself.

I bought some new clothes but kept the old ones, the larger size, until I read that I should give them away. Apparently, by keeping them, I'm inadvertently mentally attracting the weight back.

I'm now into decluttering my place. I've read that when we look around our home and feel light and decluttered we start feeling lighter in our body and will shed the weight. I never knew there was a correlation between my cluttered home and my heavy body or I would have gotten rid of everything years ago! Zen home, Zen body... hmm.

If I really listen to my thoughts, I will never date again. But part of me feels like it's time to get back out there, so I signed up with an online dating site. I need some distraction.

My idea of doing calming yoga is sitting cross-legged on the couch in front of the TV and lifting popcorn to my mouth. I know I have to resist that kind of temporary comfort, but I really need something to help slow down my brain. I decided to explore a yoga studio near work. I went to a Yin class where you hold one pose for five minutes. Turns out it was more of a yawn class. I thought it would be an easy introduction for me and the poses weren't hard, but it was so boring and the instructor's voice sounded so phoney as she dragged out her words, "Nooowww... release what you're holding and let in light..." It was as though she was talking and walking in slow motion.

It was excruciating. And at the end of the class, she started chanting in Sanskrit and the rest of the participants were chanting along with her. I didn't understand a word of it. I thought why not chant in English? Maybe yoga is not for me.

The only good thing about it was that there was a hot guy on one of the mats. I was feeling better about my body even though I still had to buy the largest size yoga pants from Lululemon. My face and neck had thinned down and my arms were more toned. I couldn't wait for the class to end so I could say hello to him. But at the end he walked out with a gorgeous Lululemon-size-two woman.

I should've tried yoga before spending so much money on a yoga outfit. Maybe I was hoping to meet a guy at yoga? I didn't know that the classes are mostly attended by women. In that class of about twenty there were only two men—and the other guy was much older. I'm not into older men, yet. A friend suggested I try a yoga-for-athletes class because there are more men in those classes. I thought, oh right! Yoga for athletes because I am sooo athletic!

Today at lunch with some friends from work, I saw Matt and his girlfriend. I couldn't breathe. Later, my friends said all the colour instantly drained out of my face. All I wanted to do was to leave the restaurant. But I didn't. I didn't want Matt to see me.

Just when I think I am moving forward something like this happens and I find myself in the same place as when he left me.

I keep thinking that once I lose the weight, I'll be happy.

But at what weight?

How many pounds?

Matt would tell me that I'm not motivated. That I never want to do much. Was my weight holding me back?

What do I want to do other than work, shop, and watch Netflix?

If I do find another man, would I be happy?

What do I want to do with my life?

I have no dreams other than losing the weight, finding a man, buying a house, and travelling. Now I'm questioning my dreams. Are these my true dreams and desires?

Is being thin the secret to happiness?

Are thin people happy?

I start hanging out with a co-worker who is into yoga. She laughed when I told her about my one and only yoga experience. She recommended that I see the emotional healing coach that she's been seeing and talk to her about the questions I've been having about what I want from my one and only life. She also explained what an emotional healing coach does. I'd never heard of it.

After a few sessions with Kathryn, the emotional healing coach, I begin to notice a physical sensation in my stomach. She calls it "a knot in my solar plexus" and I realize that I've been feeling it since I was a teenager. She tells me it's connected to an emotional trauma that I've been holding in my body.

I wasn't conscious of it, but I could feel it and I would binge-eat to make it go away. Kathryn guides me to dive right into that physical sensation and I sense it as a dark, gooey-blob sensation.

I identify it as the anger I felt toward my parents and the deep feelings of hatred I've carried all these years for my uncle who sexually abused my sister, Mandy.

Kathryn and I work on releasing the emotion and in time it does become less intense and I'm not binge-eating as often. But the gooey-blob is still there. She encourages me to explore it and I finally find words to describe it. It becomes more specific and I learn that my anger and hatred toward my family is only one aspect of my suffering. More important is the anger and hatred I've been carrying toward my own body from an emotional trauma I thought I had dealt with a long time ago.

When I was fourteen, I had a boyfriend named Tyler. We had only been dating for a couple of weeks. We kissed and held hands. I was so happy and proud that he asked me out. He would come over to my house. My parents liked him and approved of his family. He was smart and played on the basketball team at school.

"Ashley gets drunk so fast, haha," Tyler would say to his friends. I had never had a drink of alcohol until I dated Tyler, but I didn't want him to know that.

One night at a party, I had too much to drink. I remember kissing Tyler, but I couldn't remember anything else until I woke up at a friend's house. There was blood between my legs. At first, I thought I'd got my period, but then my friend told me what happened. Toward the end of the party, she started looking for me and found me naked and passed out alone in a room.

The gossip about that night started to spread at school. The sight of Tyler became nauseating to me. He grinned when he saw me. An ugly kind of smirk.

Not long after, he started dating another girl and walking hand-in-hand with her at school. Suddenly, other boys started to say hello to me. I became popular with the boys and in a sick way I enjoyed my popularity, even though it was for a terrible reason. The girls whispered "slut" when I walked by and my girlfriends started avoiding me, so I joined a new circle of girls who were more accepting of this new me.

After Mandy's sexual abuse, my parents sent me to see a therapist. I couldn't believe the uncle I adored would do such a thing to Mandy. I was fifteen when I finally shared the secret of my rape experience with the therapist. Then I started putting on weight and continued being promiscuous. I went to therapy for many years, and I thought I had forgiven Tyler.

Kathryn said, "There is a false belief that in order to heal we must forgive those who hurt us. There is only one person that you must forgive, Ashley, and that is *you*!"

There has always been a stigma attached to girls who are sexually active and my parents were typical of their generation, shaming and labelling them as sluts. I have an image of my mother's face burned in my mind, her downturned mouth and disapproving eyes sizing me up as I came down the stairs, dressed up to go out with my friends. "That top is very inappropriate, Ashley. It shows too much. That skirt is so short and tight."

I didn't tell my parents when Tyler raped me because I knew they would blame me for wearing slutty clothes and getting drunk. Tyler was well-developed for a fourteen-year-old boy. He was tall and had broad sexy shoulders and he knew it. He took off his shirt whenever we lay on the grass or when he played basketball with his friends.

Did I rape him?

Did he ask for it when he was showing his sexy naked chest?

He knew he was hot and that many girls wanted him.

Oh, and how about his tight jeans showing his bulging dick?

Did I grab his dick when he wore those jeans? Was he asking for it?

Of course I didn't tell my mom when I was raped.

Of course I blamed myself.

Of course I made excuses for Tyler. He was young and drunk.

Of course I hated myself.

Rather than love and care for and heal my body that had been invaded, I chose to hate it and to hate my parents, especially my mom, for slut-shaming girls. What my parents didn't understand is that people like them and all the others in our culture who make the girl the culprit rather than the victim of a rape are unwittingly endorsing the behaviour of boys like Tyler and men like my uncle who ultimately get away with their crimes.

Although my soul was broken when Mandy was sexually abused by my uncle, a part of me felt a release in a very innocent way, knowing that it doesn't matter what we wear or how we act because we girls, we women, cannot be protected from sick, perverted boys and men.

After Kathryn and I worked through my traumas and my emotional obstacles, she started bringing my attention to manifestation.

Who is Ashley without her past traumas and stories?

What are my heartfelt desires?

I don't know what I want. What are my heartfelt desires? All I can think is that I want to be in nature with trees, moss, flowers, birds soaring in the sky, and ocean waves cracking my heart wide open.

I've started going for hikes on weekends. I pack a lunch and go on a day hike with me—just me. All those years I begged Matt to come for a hike and he refused because I was too out of shape and slowed him down. He couldn't get his heart rate up high enough.

When no one is around and it is only me and the trees and animals I let out my anger and hurt—I scream into the sky.

Letting out the feelings that no longer serve me by screaming also keeps the bears and cougars away.

FUCK YOU, MATT.

YOU HATED EVERYTHING ABOUT ME.

AND FUCK ME... YES, FUCK YOU, ASHLEY, FOR GIVING SO MUCH POWER TO MATT, FOR BEGGING FOR HIS LOVE AND APPROVAL.

I read the book *Wild* and watched the movie. I like the book better. It's inspiring. And I felt encouraged, thinking that at least I'm not as fucked up as her, the author, when she started hiking the trail unprepared and all by herself. But I am fucked up enough that I need to do something to scare myself.

I've chosen a sheltered, safe life and look what happened—I ended up with forty pounds of unwanted fat, a broken heart and no self-worth.

Sorry, Mom and Dad. You can worry about me for a week. I'm hiking the West Coast Trail of the Pacific Rim National Park Reserve with no one but myself! This hike is not recommended for me, a beginner backpacker!

Please let it be sunny. I hate being cold and damp.

And especially when I'll be climbing the ladders. I really hope it will be dry and not slippery.

How will I climb the long ladders with my pack on my back?

It did rain, though, most days!

My socks were soaked most of the time. At night, I dried them out over a fire I built; the smell was disgusting. There were times that I was really scared. There were times that I cried. There were times that I felt lonely. And there were times that I wanted to ask Mom and Dad to send a rescue team to get me.

There's a good reason why this trail is not recommended for beginners.

I envied the couples who were doing it together. I was obsessed with checking out if the women were overweight or not.

Was it only Matt who wouldn't do things with me because I was heavy? There were women of all sizes on the trail. Women my size with their husbands or partners.

Matt did not love me and that's why he didn't want to do things with me.

Matt was fucking someone else.

What about if he wasn't just fucking her?

What if he fell in love with her?

Oh… that really hurts. It's easier to blame him, the other woman, and my body than to *blame the person who I have become.*

Was he bored living with me?

What if he wanted something more from his life and I was holding him back?

I just wish he'd had the guts to talk to me. Tell me what he really felt.

Sure, if you need to leave, then leave, but leave me without cheating on me.

When did people lose the ability to courageously confront one another? To speak heart to heart? To tell their authentic truth, no matter what?

How can two people fall in love and live together for twelve years and not have the decency or the respect or, at the very least, the mercy, to tell the truth when they fall out of love?

I did finish the hike! I don't recommend it to any beginner backpacker.

My butt needed kicking and the West Coast Trail did it! Now coming back to my routine life is so depressing. I did not carry a mirror with me on the trail. It was incredibly precious and freeing not seeing my body in the mirror and therefore not judging it. The other bonus was not weighing myself on the scale.

Now, I miss my nightly rituals on the trail.

MY FIRE CEREMONY

I made small twigs with my knife.

I held them over my fire to watch them burn.

Each twig represented a thought,

Painful and grateful,

I sent my wounds into the earth with the ash,

And my gratitude went up with the smoke into the star-filled universe

Until the small pile of twigs perished.

I saved like crazy in the two years since I did the West Coast Trail so I could come and do this pilgrimage—the Camino de Santiago in Spain. I have been the prisoner of my stories, my body, and my past for way too long. I'm dreaming of detachment from all of it. Detachment from my thoughts, my stories, and mostly from the dream I've had since I was in my early twenties of a nice man, a big house, and kids.

I gave up the dream of having kids when Matt refused to have any. Is the dream of having a man and a house my dream, or is it a generic dream most women have?

Do young women of other cultures have the same dream? I had a beautiful dollhouse growing up. Who started the game of playing house? Pretending to pour tea, hold a baby, feed a baby doll with a bottle?

I no longer believe that our existence here is an accident. I believe that we are here for a purpose. What was my purpose when I was born? Before I was taught that women's bodies are only sexy at certain sizes and shapes, that girls play house, get married, and have babies? And that men rule the world?

Here I come, Camino de Santiago.

One month of walking unplugged, except for a few emails to my parents. I savour the hours of walking in silence and the company at mealtimes when I meet other pilgrims and hear their whys.

There is so much time in a day, now that I'm not on my cell, texting, or checking Facebook, Instagram, and Snapchat. Only my thoughts and me!

I've made up a game. When I catch myself thinking the same thoughts over and over, the stories that have been repeating in my head for most of my life, I stop whatever I'm doing and I breathe deeply. On the second breath, I whisper *May I be here*. On the third breath, I look around and ask, *What is calling me?* It might be a tree, a bird, a river, a pond, a cloud, or the genuine smile of a fellow pilgrim.

Sometimes, I stop at a tree to pray. Other times, I stop by a bridge or a rock or a bench that people kindly put in front of their yards for pilgrims to sit on.

My prayers emerge from my heart and not from any religion.

Whatever is calling me, I sit beside it or lean on it or touch it. And whatever I'm feeling—sadness, sorrow, anger, or hurt—I close my eyes and visualize it leaving my body and going away. It's the best feeling watching the blocked, triggered emotions fly away from me. Sometimes I imagine putting my unwanted emotions in a hot-air balloon; I watch it drift far, far away.

Now that I'm not as stuck in my own stories I have an ear for other people's. Sometimes their stories penetrate deep into my heart. Last night at dinner, a pilgrim who is a journalist told us stories about Syrian refugees. Whenever I used to hear horrible stories of war and terrorist attacks in other countries I always felt so grateful to be living in Canada. I thought we Canadians have our challenges, but nothing like what so many people around the world endure. But now I no longer feel the same gratitude for living in a peaceful country like Canada. How can I?

Canada is not Syria, Iran, or America, but hundreds of unmarked graves of Indigenous children were found in the grounds around former residential schools in Canada—my country!

The suffering we caused for the First Nations is our suffering: the energy of their suffering overlaps ours.

Kathryn taught me the difference between fake gratitude and authentic gratitude. I'm truly grateful for moving forward in my life even though there are times I take a few steps back, and that's okay.

At night the rooms in the hostel are pitch-black. At bedtime, I use a flashlight to get to the bathroom. One night, a noise woke me up. Moon was lighting the room through the skylight and I looked toward the noise. I saw a shiny thing moving. I sat up on my bed and shone my flashlight at it. I was afraid it was a big, fat rat. It stopped moving. Oh, no… it was someone's ass! I was so shocked that I didn't immediately turn the flashlight off. He turned and I saw his face and then hers. I actually recognized them. I had dinner with them and a few other pilgrims that night.

They were older, maybe mid-sixties, close to my parents' age. It made me wonder if my parents were still doing *it*? Yikes, I didn't want to think about that right then. I really had to pee, but I was too embarrassed to walk by their bed.

Ooh, this handsome guy is walking toward me. Is he really coming to my table and looking at me?

"Are you waiting for someone?" he asks.

I'm so slow answering that he asks again, "May I join you?"

My throat is shut. I manage a smile and introduce myself.

What I really want to ask him is, "Are you really here all by yourself? No wife, no partner?"

This hot guy's name is Xavier and he's making small talk with me in his charming Australian accent. I can't really track what he's saying because I'm totally distracted by his deeply tanned skin and chocolate brown eyes. I'm such a loser.

For a moment we are alone in my dreamy bubble until it is burst by a swarm of women who sit down at our communal table and begin buzzing like bees over him.

They were just shy of drooling over him, but how can I blame them? At least they're speaking, unlike me who was spellbound and couldn't manage to utter a word. Let him think that I'm one of those contemplative, intelligent women who doesn't just blab, blab, blab.

I have a few glasses of wine hoping it will help my charming personality emerge, haha; no luck. The other women are loud and doing their best to hold Xavier's attention. To my surprise, though, he keeps turning to include me in the conversation. I'm in shock. I have *never* been the centre of attention of such a smoulderingly sexy man. Let me say that again: *never*! And there are many attractive, athletic-looking women at our table who are obviously lusting after him. But Xavier seems interested in me. Hmmm… maybe miracles *do* happen on the Camino trail!

When we are leaving the table, he leans in and asks me what time I plan to start my walk in the morning and whether he can join me.

I want to say that I would slow him down. I really want to ask why me and not one of those gorgeous women. Does he think I'm loaded? Is he after money? Should I tell him that I used up all my saving to do this pilgrimage? But what I really need to say is that I walk solo in silence. Instead, I happily accept his company and excitedly plan our hike together!

I can't sleep. I'm so excited. The shock of him being interested in me. Oh, I so want to have sex with him. Now I'm horny. I can't even masturbate here—everyone would hear me!

What can I talk about on our hike so I don't make a fool of myself? He says he has been on a spiritual journey for many years and has a spiritual teacher. Hmm, maybe I should tell him I have a spiritual teacher, too. Does an emotional healing coach count as a spiritual teacher?

There have been so many conversations at the dinner table about this guru and that guru. I'm confused about the difference between a guru and a spiritual teacher and about many other subjects that come up at the table. He'd lived in an ashram in India for six months. Does zoning out on Netflix count as a retreat? If you added up the hours I've watched Netflix I'm sure it would total well over a year. So there—I had been on a Netflix retreat for a year.

So many thoughts. I'm too excited to sleep!

I try to breathe to calm my mind. I hear Kathryn's voice, "Breathe. Breathe in for a count of four.... Hold your breath for a count of two.... Breathe out for a count of eight...."

Thoughts... What did I do in my life? Worked, stepped on a scale every day, checked my weight, found clothes that hid my belly rolls. I felt happy when I found a nice guy; I felt miserable when the guy left me. Oh yeah, I did go to university and got an education and I have a well-paid job in marketing.

Okay, no more thoughts. I must sleep.

Breathe....

Thoughts....

Thoughts....

Breathe....

Unlike at last night's dinner, today on our walk there is hardly any conversation about his spiritual accomplishments and, to my relief, he doesn't ask me any questions about my spiritual teacher or what denomination I belong to. Up until last night

I thought Buddhism was just one thing. I had no idea that there were so many branches of it. Xavier wears a mala bead bracelet and has a tattoo on his left arm of "Om" in Sanskrit. I guess those were the reasons that the women kept showing off their knowledge of Buddhism and asking him questions. I confess to him that the only thing I know about Buddhism is that I had a Buddha statue on my front porch because it looked good and was fashionable. Last summer someone stole it . I didn't even notice that it was missing until there was bird poo on my porch and when I was cleaning the mess, I noticed the Buddha statue was gone.

This is Xavier's story as he told it to me.

"Six years ago, my father died. Up until then, I was a CEO of a company and making a lot of money. I'd supported my mom and dad for years. I loved cars, women, and lived in a luxurious penthouse in the heart of Sydney. I didn't know what was driving me to all of that. Maybe I hated growing up poor. Maybe it was my way of telling my dad, 'Fuck you for screwing up your family by raising us in poverty—look how easy it is to provide all this for your family.'

"I felt nothing when I found out he died of pneumonia. I felt the bugger deserved it. But when he was buried, I just sat beside his grave, not crying, but not hating him either, just sitting.

"My mom said, 'Son, let's go, people are waiting.' But I couldn't move.

"I told her to take my sister and go see to the guests. A couple of co-workers came over and asked if they could help. I had no close friends. My close friends were the women I slept with, but none of them were there except for one who thought she was my girlfriend. She had no idea I was seeing other women while I was with her. I asked her to leave, too. Since then I have not been back to work. I stopped using drugs and I stopped having sex.

"I had had so much hatred for my dad until then. Once my hatred was buried with him, I felt lost and broken. I had been broken all along, but sex and drugs blocked me from seeing it.

"I missed that bugger, my dad. The most unsettling part about losing him was realizing that even though I thought I had it all and knew who I was, in truth I had no clue. A thought overwhelmed me—Who am I without the hatred I had for my dad?"

Whenever I went on an adventure, I hoped to meet someone. But it never happened. Until now. Let me pinch myself. I'm not dreaming this is real. Xavier is real!

My prince charming is a recovered drug and sex addict and is still on his path to healing. I'm a recovered food addict. We are both on a pilgrimage, praying for balance and a taste of happiness in our lives without numbing ourselves with food, drugs, sex, and alcohol.

Opposites don't attract—but addicts sure do!

"Ash, the sex addiction was the hardest to quit. I stopped taking drugs and chose not to hang out with people who do drugs so I wouldn't be dragged into it. But staying celibate is another story. I've been celibate for two years, but I don't wish to stay celibate for the rest of my life."

With a food addiction, I can't choose not to eat, or stop hanging out around the people who eat.

After a few nights of staying at the hostels, Xavier suggests we get our own room. We are still sleeping in different beds. I know too well about addiction and although I want him so badly, I don't want to tempt him if he isn't ready. It took a while before he lay beside me in my bed the whole night.

"I actually feel a strong pain." He points at his groin. "I haven't felt this for a long time. I've been afraid to feel it."

Until now I haven't seen my naked body during the pilgrimage. But tonight, in our private bathroom there is a mirror. My eyes immediately zoom on my fat belly and the cellulite on my legs. I wrap a towel around me so he doesn't see my naked body as I leave the shower.

I remember too well when friends and family gathered at Thanksgiving and Christmas dinners and the men—when they were asked if they would like a turkey leg or the breast—would say, "Oh, I'm a breast man" or "I'm a leg man." I also remember too well the grins on their faces. Matt was a leg man. I do not have large breasts so I was relieved when he said he was a leg man. My legs looked good in leggings and jeans at that time, but not in shorts: damn cellulite! So many years of programming and so many painful years of judging my own body and listening to that self-deprecating voice telling me, "You are fat, ugly, imperfect."

The way Xavier looked at me and touched my body was like he worshipped it and, at the same time, it was like he was looking and touching something way more precious than a body. Such an unfamiliar feeling to be revered. Free of thought, wholly absorbed in pleasure and touch, our lovemaking that night felt like a sacrament. I have never had a more erotic or divinely sensual experience in my life.

Matt was not the first man who had left me. I'd had other long-term relationships before him and I repeated the same pattern in all of them. At the start, I felt vibrant. I exercised, I joined them in their activities. Then slowly, like a flower without water, I wilted. I put on weight and felt exhausted all the time. I would go back to watching TV and my only exercise was walking back and forth to the pantry for snacks.

And when they left, I threw a pity party, blaming them and everything on my body image! Was it true that each one of them left me because I was overweight? Or did they leave me because I was depressed, unmotivated, uninspired and I didn't love and respect myself? No self-worth.

The moment I felt I was falling in love, I would imagine our wedding. When I was younger, I dreamed of a glorious wedding dress and the splendour of a big wedding. As I got older and had a few broken relationships I imagined smaller weddings and a more casual wedding dress. Here I go again, imagining Xavier proposing, me saying yes, the two of us wearing white, our bare feet standing on the beach.

I'm doing it again! Universe, please hand me an extra-strength remote control. I need to pause and delete my wedding scene.

I don't want to do this to Xavier. Not him. He is too precious to me. Please let me not do this to him or me.

If the remote control stops my imagination from playing the "Getting Married" movie, then what movie do I want to play? The movie of me hiking, walking on a pilgrimage, seeing the world. And what else?

What movie do I play when I'm not hiking, walking, and exploring the world?

What movie do I play in my everyday life?

I don't want to just live for the days or the weeks that I go hiking. What work would I do if I didn't need money?

What are my heartfelt desires?

Who is the true Ashley?

I don't want to lose myself again.

Follow your dreams.

Manifest your heartfelt desires.

Find your life purpose.

Up until three years ago, my life purpose was to shop online, watch Netflix, with supplies of chocolate, salt and vinegar chips, cheese and crackers, and wine on hand. Pretty simple and sometimes still appealing. I still don't know what I want. What are my heartfelt desires? My dreams?

What I do know is since I met him, I want to be with him every second of my life. If I believed in reincarnation, I would believe that Xavier and I were in love in one of our past lives, but we were forced apart by some tragic accident or event. I feel that something deep in me has been looking for him for so many lifetimes.

But what if I'm just infatuated with his hot, sexy body, his dark eyes, and oh, his accent is so arousing.

I'm sick and tired of being single. Maybe we'll get married and I will stop working. I will live happily ever after, not having to go to another marketing conference and pretending that I love my work. I like the money that I make. It pays the bills. But, if I marry Xavier… I'm so quitting my job.

It's so easy to fall in love and fit myself right into his life. Believe me, I did it before in my other relationships. I can see myself following him into whatever he's doing. I'll go to the ashram with him. I will adopt his spiritual teacher as mine and wear mala beads. Get an "Om" tattoo just like his.

Xavier, I'm not breaking up with you. I'm breaking up with the old Ashley. Tomorrow, I'll continue doing what I've come here to do—to walk a solo pilgrimage and heal. I will find a tree and let it hear me crying or sobbing. Telling it all about my love for you and my heartbreak.

It's time for Ashley to see what Xavier sees in her.

Last week I sobbed while saying goodbye to Xavier. And then I danced the dance of freedom escaping from the prison of my limiting beliefs. The limiting belief that if I lose weight I will find a man who will finally love me the way I want to be loved and I will marry him.

When we said goodbye, Xavier handed me a letter and asked me not to read it until after I completed the pilgrimage. Today, my one month on the Camino de Santiago is up.

Ash,

A creek ran near my childhood home. It was a favourite hangout place for us kids in summertime. The creek meant more to me than just a creek—it seemed that I'd known it for eternity. I enjoyed playing in the creek with the neighbourhood kids, but I especially loved it when I could be there alone. There was a spot where the creek meandered and the water was shallow and slow-moving. I lay there with my arms stretched open and my eyes closed; floating and sometimes just sinking. Either way I felt I was at home—a home unlike any other home I knew. My body, the water, the soil was all one. There was no separation between my skin and the skin of water. We blended into one.

When I lost myself to drugs and sex I also lost my memory of the creek. During those years of addiction there were times when I would pause for a second and wonder what it was that I was deeply missing, but then I would get distracted and ended up numbing myself out.

My spiritual teacher once suggested that I try to remember the things I did in my childhood that brought me joy. The reason for this practice was that in our childhood we are more aligned with our authentic self, but as we grow, as a result of all the programming and traumas, we become separated from our core, our true essence. Going back to our childhood memories and remembering what we truly enjoyed and loved brings back the essence of how it feels to live an authentic life.

I hardly remembered any childhood memory because of all the traumas I suffered then. Then I was in the ashram and one day during meditation the vision of the creek came to me. Ah, the memory was so vivid that I could hear the creek running, so loving, calming, and freeing. Ash, you are that creek to me. You are not my creek. You are not my Ash. You are not my lifeline. You are my soul line. There is no separation between my skin and yours, no ending, no beginning.

You asked me once to write down my mantra for you—this is the mantra that has been protecting me from my mind and my thoughts.

"Om mani padme hum.

"I bow to the jewel in the lotus of the heart.

"Om."

It's in Sanskrit though, haha. I do remember you saying how you felt in the yoga class when they were chanting in Sanskrit. I know I can say it in English, but when I say it in Sanskrit, it gives me a high better than any drug.

What it means for me is "Bow to love and do not fear it."

It's not me who loves you. The love that my physical being can give you comes with expiration—it's my essence, my core being who has fallen in love with you and it is there that we unite with the infinite.

I don't know how many lifetimes it has been since we were lovers. All I know is that I found you in this lifetime and I hope our get-together this time around wasn't meant to be this short.

Xavier

Grateful-for-Liam Cards

I WISH I'D said, "I love you" more often.

I didn't know how to handle your depression. Therapy and drugs were what seemed the right thing to do and you did seem to be getting better. But clearly it was just a mask.

And now that you're not here all I'm thinking is what could I have done differently.

Oh, Liam, where are you!?

I had no tools to deal with my shit and your depression. I just kept thinking that I'd failed you as a mother. I couldn't see that I was sick, too.

My eating disorder.

My own depression.

For the first few months after you disappeared, we lied to everyone and said you went to Europe. Eventually we told the truth. But still, I couldn't talk about it.

There was no news.

Nothing to say.

My heart was broken, Liam, and I couldn't talk about that. I just exercised and stayed busy and worked and tried to be a good mom to Kate and Josh.

I never knew what love was until I held you in my arms.
When people talked about falling in love
I couldn't relate.
I didn't know what that felt like.
But the moment I saw you
My baby boy,
Liam,
I tasted love.

You were only three when we were walking in the park and you pointed at a bird and said, "What's that?"

And I said, "It's a sparrow."

Then you spotted another one and said, "That one was a sparrow. What's this one?"

I bought a book of birds and we started learning the names together: starlings, junco, finch …

You and I were the only ones who liked to watch *The Wizard of Oz*. And every time you would ask me who I wanted to be, I always chose the cowardly lion and you always said, "Mom, why do you want to be him? You already have so much courage."

You saw things in me that no one else saw. Not even me.

Never me.

Where is that courage now?

I'm terrified.

Who will I be without fear?

Will I have the courage to find you, Liam?

Will I have the courage to watch *The Wizard of Oz* without you?

I realize now how much I was in-the-box and how you were so out-of-the-box.

My friends' kids were going to law school and medical school and engineering universities and you were still living at home, bartending with no plans for a future. I couldn't accept it and I was really disappointed in you.

You would go for long hikes with our dog Toffee and come home stoned. I know you saw my disapproval and felt my judgment. You would flip me the peace sign and say, "Long live MJ!"

I'm trying to get out of the box. I wish you were here to help. Maybe we would smoke a joint together. Maybe it could help me sleep.

Hey, Liam, Long Live MJ!

Love Mom.

P.S. I don't give a shit about my friends' kids' careers.

Just want them to be happy and healthy.

Another Christmas without you.

And this year I'm not going to cry in silence thinking of you or try to escape my pain with an elaborate meal and listen to everyone obsessing about their weight gain and New Year's resolutions.

Fuck New Year's resolutions.

Your dad and Kate and Josh aren't happy about my plan, but this year I'm helping the homeless. I'm working with a group that delivers meals on Christmas Day. I'm making my best dishes to share with the homeless people. There are so many of them. It's heartbreaking to see.

I gave Dad the Christmas recipes and said, "You make the meal for a change… ha!"

I started seeing an emotional healing coach. Her name is Kathryn!

I was so flat, Liam, like a bottle of wine with no character. No body. Yes, I still like my wine!

I'm only fifty-two. I had no passion for anything. I knew after last Christmas—I invited thirty people for dinner and I couldn't feel a thing—that something had to change. All those holidays… Thanksgiving and Christmas and New Years… I invited so many people to try and fill this void—this void of you not being here.

I wanted to feel appreciated with my life like an exquisitely aged wine. I wanted to be opened, to breathe, and be savoured. The thought of staying bottled up for another minute, let alone the rest of my life, had finally become intolerable.

Kathryn calls you my catalyst. She says you turn my grape juice into wine. She has encouraged me to surround myself with friends who listen and empathize and don't try to fix me or solve my problems or bore me with new age positive thinking.

I call that stuff SBS… Spiritual Bypass Shit.

I feel like I am finally acting like my true, authentic self. Turns out your mom has a potty mouth, Liam. Ha! Imagine that! I'm hoping you are laughing with me. I know I was so adamant about not swearing in the house—fuck, did you push that button, you swore all the time. Now look at me!

So, I choose you as my friend. My empathetic friend I can share this heartbreak with. Lucky guy... this sounds so sad, but I don't have a single person who will just listen with empathy, so you are it.

Well, Liam, my good empathetic friend. Here it is... my true-heart rant.

HEY, FRIENDS... YA YOU... I HATE IT WHEN YOU SHUT ME UP WITH THAT SBS CRAP.

I CAN'T JUST LET GO AND MOVE ON. MY SON IS GONE AND I AM SO INSANELY WORRIED ABOUT HIM EVERY SECOND OF EVERY DAY THAT I CANNOT REST. I CANNOT SLEEP. I DON'T TALK ABOUT MY SON ANYMORE BECAUSE I CAN'T STAND TO HEAR THAT SAME OLD SBS ANYMORE. HEARING "YOU MUST THINK OF YOURSELF" AND "THINK OF KATE AND JOSH" MAKES ME FEEL PATHETIC AND WEAK BECAUSE I CAN'T...

I CAN'T LET GO!

AND I WANT TO SCREAM IN YOUR FACES.

SCREAM SO LOUD IT WILL MAKE THE CLOUDS PART AND THE SKY RUMBLE.

I JUST WANT TO HEAR MY SON'S VOICE

I JUST WANT TO HUG MY SON

I WANT TO HEAR HIM PLAY HIS GUITAR

GOD... UNIVERSE... JESUS... WHATEVER... WHOEVER YOU ARE, PLEASE LET ME SEE MY SON AGAIN.

This is what bugs me the most:

just let it go

you've got to move on

think positive thoughts

don't worry, I'm sure he's fine.

I hear this crap and I think to myself… really? You're sure he's fine? Have you gone looking for him? Wouldn't you worry if you were me?

Ugggghhhhh!!!!!!!!!!!

See… triggered.

And this one:

it's time to start thinking about yourself and enjoy your life.

Is it?

Really?

Kathryn says that you are my guru.

From now on, I will be thinking of you as "Liam, my Guru."

She says that you are like a lantern in my dark nights.

I meditate now and when I do, my mind goes calm and I can feel you. Your soul and mine are together as one. And it's *magnificent*.

I want that feeling to last forever.

When you left, you asked us not to contact you, but we did. We had to. Then you changed your email address and we didn't have a mailing address. We contacted your closest friends and they told us that you had stopped communicating with them.

You aren't dead.

You aren't missing.

Your birthdays come and go. I always make sure that the day is completely planned so I won't be alone. I don't want to risk falling apart and maybe calling someone and asking for help or admitting that I can't stand this.

I've boxed up your things and shoved them into the crawl space. I can't go through your things. I can't give them away.

Your birthday is a month away. I've decided that I will open one of your boxes then. Some of them contain your drawings and paintings and some your favourite sweaters... the handmade wool sweaters that I bought for you at Christmas fairs. I can still see you as a teenager wearing your baggy wool sweater and sitting in front of the fireplace, reading, and eating Christmas cookies.

I've asked Grandma and Grandpa over. Your dad and sister and brother were shocked when I told them that I wanted to have a birthday dinner for you. Kate and Josh never talk about you to me. Perhaps they only feel the wall that I have built around me. I just did that to protect them so they don't see how broken I am inside.

Kathryn says being vulnerable is empowering. I totally believe that now. All these years I thought I was being strong by not showing my emotions, but that didn't get me anywhere.

I don't believe that time heals all wounds.

I am letting myself be vulnerable on your birthday. I am willing to risk breaking down. I want Josh and Kate to see all of me.

All these years I've been hiding. You never knew that I had an eating disorder since I was a teenager. I'm exhausted from hiding.

I'm going to make your favourite dish and cake and have a family birthday dinner for you.

I know in my heart that you are not dead.

It's time for me to start acting like you're alive!

I was walking along the beach when I noticed a box of ripe red tomatoes and this young guy sitting next to it. He had a tent set up, but it wasn't a camping spot and I wondered how he managed to avoid getting kicked off the beach. The tomatoes were so ripe and red, and I wondered where he had gotten them because there weren't any at the farmers' market yet. So I asked him where he got them and he said, "Dumpster diving."

He offered to let me take a few. We started talking. He said that he's chosen a lifestyle of "homelessness." He reminded me of you. He was smart and passionate while he talked about corporations and the corruption of democracy.

I regret my resistance and my views towards homelessness. I believed by giving them money we enable their drug and alcohol addiction. I remember our heated discussion. I still hear your voice, "Fuck, do you guys really believe that addiction is a fucking choice?" I still see the anger in your face and hear the anger in your voice.

This "have no regrets" thing isn't working for me.

I regret not slowing down and enjoying the simple things with you.

I'm working on forgiving myself for that. And for hiding so long. My eating disorder wasn't obvious, so I could keep it a secret. When I got pregnant with you I decided to give up the laxatives because I was afraid you wouldn't get the nourishment you needed.

I stopped drinking the laxative, but replaced the obsession with exercise. I had nightmares about getting fat during my pregnancy. The fear of getting fat was my sole motivation for running, hiking, swimming, taking exercise classes. I weighed myself every day. My goal was to keep my weight gain with you to under twenty-five pounds. And I did.

I can still hear you asking me, "Mom, can I come hiking with you?"

I didn't want to take you with me. You stopped and looked at every tiny bug, collected differently shaped leaves, and you brought your bird book and waited at every pond to look for frogs. Sunday was the only day I could do a trail run and burn as many calories as possible. My heart rate, the distance I could go, the fat and calories I burned were more important to me than spending time with you. I always felt so guilty that I did take you sometimes, but you moved so slowly.

Kathryn invited me to join a *mindful* hiking group. They go on Sundays. A Buddhist friend of hers leads the walk. I was nervous because I didn't know anyone, and I don't know anything about Buddhism. I was told that I could only use my phone for photos—nothing else. I couldn't measure distance or count calories.

These mindful hikes remind me so much of the hikes I took with you. Liam, the Guru. You naturally knew how to slow down and be *here.*

During our hikes, we observe our thoughts and take in everything around us. Last week we saw a bear cross a ravine some distance away and we just sat down for five minutes and watched and breathed. I was scared at first, but the ravine was deep enough that we could have run away if he'd given chase.

I didn't like these hikes at first because they were so slow, but I am beginning to appreciate them and enjoy them more.

Liam, I am going to remember the times that we did go hiking together and not feel guilty for the times when I said no. I am grateful that I took pictures of you during our slow hikes... you, holding leaves up to show me, your big beautiful smile with your teeth missing and your brown hair shining in the sun when you were seven. And the one by the pond where you are swishing a stick through the water looking for frogs. If only I could have another slow hike with you, Liam.

I bought you a junior Monopoly game one Christmas. You were forever asking me, "Mom, do you want to play Monopoly?"

I thought it would be fun for the family, but you only wanted to play with me. I didn't like playing with just the two of us... it took so long.

The next Christmas, I got you Chinese Checkers. You spent all Christmas Day learning how to play.

Your dad wasn't into board games so you taught me all the rules and we played together. You played the blue marbles and I played the green. The marbles were pretty and I liked that the game moved faster than chess, but we still had to think and develop a strategy. You finally figured out how to slow me down to sit and play a game with you. When Dad and Kate wanted to join in you said, "No, you should've joined Mom and me when we were beginners. Now you will slow down the game." You only ever wanted to play with me.

After you started taking the antidepressants you never wanted to play games anymore. I packed away the Chinese Checkers.

Yesterday I took the game out and set it up where we used to play. I held a few of the blue marbles in my hand and started to cry. Dad said, "Honey, don't you think this is too hard for you?" He isn't used to seeing me vulnerable. I was always so perfect at hiding my emotions.

I'm playing Chinese Checkers again. My skills were rusty at the beginning. My imaginary opponent is playing the golden marbles. I won't play the blue marbles until I play again with you.

Liam, you were my Zen master all along. You were always showing me ways to slow down. Now I sit and play Chinese Checkers all by myself. You planted the love of this game in me.

Dad offered to play and I said no. He said that I was acting just like you. That you never wanted to play with him either, and then we both laughed. That was the first time in eight years that we talked about you and laughed.

Who the *fuck* is Rachel?

Liam, I have never asked myself this question before.

Who am I? I'm Rachel. I'm a wife, a mother. I was a senior account manager at the bank and now I'm retired. But who am I really and what the fuck do I want from this life and where am I heading?

I am someone who had thought about suicide again and again and again, but kept deciding to live. Even during my pregnancy with you, I entertained the thought of suicide. But once I saw you and you wrapped your little fingers around mine, I knew that I could not take my life. Now I know that I was suffering from depression all those years. And all those years I felt so guilty for not loving you and Kate and Josh enough. I always thought to myself, "If I love my children, then why am I not happy? Why do I not want to spend more time at home to cook and bake for my kids like other moms?"

Now I know that because of the love I had for the three of you, I hung in, I kept myself busy and distracted so that I wouldn't kill myself.

When you were diagnosed with depression, it somehow gave me permission to admit to my own. I went on antidepressants, too. It has been a few years now since I stopped taking them. I thought then that life was so horrible. It wasn't until after you left that I realized what *horrible* really feels like, not knowing if my son is alive or dead.

I am going to find you, Liam. But first, I am going to find me.

I'm starting to wake up, Liam. I'm starting to remember who I am.

I had always been the beautiful, shy little girl.

My life was perfect until my teacher at school told my parents that I was too shy and said, "You should work with Rachel on her social skills."

My best friend Sylvia and I were both quiet. I liked to play at her house because her parents were kind and thoughtful. My parents had a big circle of noisy, snobby friends and my mom loved to host big dinner parties. She wanted me to be more like her friends' daughters, to act like a little lady, and say the right things when adults asked me questions.

She was thrilled when I started hanging out with my new friend Jennifer. What she didn't know was that I learned from Jennifer how to use the liquid laxatives. She was not a true friend, but for some reason I wanted her approval. I even bought the same clothes as her, but in different colours so she wouldn't get angry. She looked down on me, but I sucked up to her anyway.

I stopped being friends with Sylvia.

I learned to be less shy, but inside I am still the same.

I freaked out on your dad when he accused me of avoiding our friends and acting like a hermit; playing Chinese Checkers by myself, meditating and reading and watching self-help videos. He is worried about me.

No one seemed to be worried when I was suicidal… not that they knew. I hid that well. But why did my parents worry when I was a happy child playing with my sweet friend Sylvia and force me to become someone that I wasn't and hang around with kids that didn't even like me?

And now your dad is worried for me because I am doing things that authentically are aligned with me!

What's wrong?

What the fuck?

Liam, grieving over you has taken me back to myself, to the shy, introverted Rachael. The real me. My authentic self!

Dad and I went to a dinner party last night. Ted and his new girlfriend were there. It's the juiciest gossip going: Ted left his wife and is having an affair with another woman. He bought her a boob job and paid for it with their joint credit card and that's how his wife found out he was cheating on her! Ugh! All our friends were there. I used to have to get wasted to tolerate Ted and his sexist remarks, but I don't drink like that anymore. It was nauseating to listen to his sexist jokes.

I remember that you called him a redneck. Liam, you were right!

I'm reading a lot of spiritual books and am seeing how all the spiritual teachers talk about seeing God in everyone. I'm having a hard time seeing God in Ted... ha! But I see God in you, Liam.

Thank you for awakening me in this lifetime.

I always dreamed that you would be a successful lawyer like your dad and his father. I envied my friends' sons who were going to reputable universities and came home for breaks with their smart, attractive girlfriends who they'd met at school. When they came to visit us and talked about their experiences at university, you just sat there, stoned, stony-faced, silent.

You took off travelling with your hippie girlfriend to pick fruit in Australia. She was named Joni after Joni Mitchell. She was a sweet girl and a nice girl, but I was ashamed and embarrassed when the two of you walked around with your ponchos, looking glassy-eyed from smoking pot.

I was angry when I packed up your poncho. I hated that thing. Then after eight years, when I opened one of your boxes, I found it. I had to put it on! I could see you so clearly, sitting in our backyard smoking weed and wearing your poncho. I didn't want to take it off.

I wear your poncho now. I wear it working in the yard and throw it on to walk out to the mailbox or to put out the garbage.

Some of the neighbours have approached me and shared memories of seeing you in your poncho. They miss you, too.

You were three when we moved into this neighbourhood. Mr. and Mrs. Martin are in their eighties now. I remember when you invited them for tea. Mr. Martin rang the doorbell and said, "Liam invited us. I hope you don't mind."

The first time they saw me wearing your poncho they held me and cried. By not grieving for you openly I've deprived the family and our friends from sharing with me their love for you.

I invite the Martins over for tea often now. Oh Liam, I couldn't believe it when they told me that they have been searching for you, too! All these years, anytime they travel, they ask the locals if they know you and watch for you on the streets and amongst the homeless people. Their love for you helps me believe that there is beauty in this life.

Your dad wanted to hire a detective to find you. I didn't agree. I thought if we found you, you would only run away again. We are the same people you abandoned before. What could we possibly offer you now that we didn't then? You knew we loved you in our own way. Didn't you?

It must not have been the love that you wanted.

I know now, Liam, that the love I had for you was contaminated with judgment, expectation, and fear—egotistical, conditional love. But that was all I knew. That was exactly how I loved myself: with judgment, and fear.

How could I offer you anything different?

I punished myself for not being perfect and you could never live up to my dreams of having a perfect son.

It has taken me two years working on forgiving myself and loving myself without judgment. All I want is to feel that I am one with this magnificent universe.

When I feel your love within me, Liam, I am the sun, the moon, the mountain, and the ocean.

My dear son, I am ready to search for you now. Because I want you to know that it is never too late to change.

It's never too late to say, "I love you."

I so want you to see who I have become because of you, so that you can gain hope for humanity.

We all have a chance to awaken when we choose to.

I was nervous to meet the detective. We did decide to hire someone to look for you. Her name is Janice. A woman in her mid-forties wearing jeans and flats and with her hair in a ponytail. She went right to the point and started asking questions and recording our answers. I gave her the Grateful-for-Liam cards and asked her to give them to you if she found you. She was concerned when she found out I had given her the original cards and I didn't have a copy of them. I told her that they were not meant to be kept and if they got lost I would write more.

I could hear Kathryn's voice in my head from our last session a year ago. She said, "Rachel, keep going to your meditation group and keep writing your Grateful-for-Liam cards."

I miss seeing Kathryn.

She started preparing me months before she finally ended our sessions, but I still wasn't ready to say goodbye. She said, "This part of your healing requires the courage to continue on the path on your own. I don't know what Rachel wants to do for the rest of her life. I have shared everything I knew that could help you on this journey. You do not need my guidance anymore.

"Now it is time for Rachel to guide Rachel."

The whole time we worked together, she never said anything about whether I should search for you or not. I really wanted her approval. All she said was, "That is part of your journey. If you listen carefully, the answer to your question is within you."

I asked her if I should send you the Grateful-for-Liam cards and rather than give me an answer, she told me about the Buddhist mandala ritual and suggested I take a workshop on how to make a mandala.

There were bowls of coloured sand. There were a few of sample patterns. The intricate patterns and colours were stunning. As the teacher explained the process and purpose of making a mandala, I understood why Kathryn wanted me to learn this skill. The process of creating and designing the mandala is from the heart and not from the mind and that was how I felt when I was writing the gratitude cards to you.

At the mandala workshop, we listened to the Buddhist monks chanting while we were making our mandalas. There were times that my thoughts would take me somewhere else, but it would only last a few seconds and then I would bring my full attention back into sifting the sand into an intricate pattern.

This process is for a single-tasking mind, not a multi-tasking mind.

The moment my attention went somewhere else, the sand was poured somewhere that it wasn't supposed to go—messing up the pattern.

At the end of the class, we took our intricately-patterned mandalas and poured them into bowls. Just like that… gone.

All that work… all that beauty… gone!

Then we took the bowls filled with sand to a nearby creek and spread the sand into it.

The making and destroying of the mandala is a lesson in the transitory nature of the material life.

Liam, you and Kate and Josh are the magnificent masterpieces that I created in my life. I have attached myself to every one of you. I thought I owned you and could shape you and keep you just the way my mind made you up to be. I will never forget the beauty of the mandala I created in that workshop. I created it with no intention to keep it and no judgment about what it looked like. I did not bring it home to show your dad or anyone else. It was about falling in love without judgment, attachment, or expectation.

The Opposite of Love is Expectation.

I love you forever

In every pond I see

I see your reflection

Your hair shining in the sun

Your adorable smile with those missing teeth

The End!

But then there is no end where there is no beginning.

Love is eternity…

Malak the Angel

HOW COULD I know that was my last chance to be with you?

I fucked it up by talking about Ryan, saying how much I loved him, even though he was a jerk and didn't respect me. I can't forgive myself. I'm a self-centred, narcissistic bitch. It's all about me, me, and more me.

Emily, if I'd known that was the last night I had with you, I would have held you all night and told you how much I love you. You mean everything to me. I would be silent and let you talk. Maybe you would've shared with me what was eating you. Killing you.

I know that you tried to kill yourself before, but I made myself believe that you got over it. I miss your laughter.

Your mom called. She used to phone whenever you didn't show up for a day or two, hoping that I had a way to find you. I always used to know where you were, the friends you hung out with. But, in the past few years I lost track. This time, when I answered she said, "Hi, sweetheart," then everything went silent.

"Is Em okay?" My heart was pounding, and I prayed for a miracle, but the second your mom stopped talking, I knew what had happened. Still, I hoped to hear that you were alive. I went silent on the phone, waiting to hear that you were still alive. I imagined you in the hospital, but I never thought I would hear what she said next.

"Kayla, sweetheart, I'm so sorry to say this on the phone, but… Emily is gone…"

I collapsed on the floor. I couldn't breathe.

I stayed with your mom for a week. My mom and dad came over every day with groceries and cooked and cleaned up. I slept in your room and wore your clothes. I made a slide show for your life celebration. Your mom chose the photos.

Everyone said that your celebration of life was beautiful, and they loved the slide show. There were so many photos of you and me. But the one of us in kindergarten was the star. We were holding each other so tightly and we looked so nervous and excited all at the same time.

There are times I'm so angry with you I call you a selfish bitch. How could you do this to your mom? Then I almost hear you whispering to me, "I did this to me, Kayla. It was too painful. I just couldn't go on any longer."

I never accepted your mental illness and it made me angry. I felt like you were just acting selfish and helpless to get attention. I wanted you to shake it off and get over it. I wanted my rock back.

You were my solid rock through all those years of elementary school and high school. I was the vulnerable one—the one who stupidly got myself into trouble. Do you remember the time I was dating Adam? You called him "the loser". You never let me get in the car with him after we'd been partying, and you always made sure I got home safe.

You were my guardian angel. Then everything flipped when you got sick.

You were always the wise one. I don't know what happened at university, but something about you changed. Your mom told me that was when your depression started. And then you got into drugs and alcohol.

I feel so guilty that I didn't stand by you in those years. You were easily irritated by people and you would snap at me for such little things. You were dating guys who were into hard drugs. I started avoiding you. I hate myself now. I failed our friendship.

Em, do you remember when you moved into our neighbourhood?

Mom brought over cookies to welcome your family.

"Kayla, honey, Emily is the same age as you," Mom said when she introduced you to me.

You and I hung out that summer, almost every day, playing in our tree house, making that fort under the pines in the empty lot at the end of our street. Our favourite part was when my dad set up a tent and let us have sleepovers in our yard. Dad read us bedtime stories using a flashlight. It was a magical summer. In September, you and I and our moms walked to school together on the first day of kindergarten.

I gasp for air while visiting my parents.

I've been feeling short of breath, but I haven't paid much attention to it. Mom is on the phone with the paramedics, "She's experiencing an asthma attack."

The ambulance brings me to the hospital and after a few hours in emergency I'm given an asthma inhaler. Even with the inhaler my symptoms get worse. Mom insists that I go see my doctor. She is concerned because I suffered severe asthma all through my childhood, but I grew out of it in my late teens. After a month of breathing tests and chest X-rays, I'm diagnosed, not with asthma, but with panic attacks.

My mom and Emily's mom, Cheryl, are worried. I've been calling in sick to work often. Mom helps me with rent money. I am living with my boyfriend Alex and we share the rent, but after Emily's death I couldn't pay for a couple of months. After a while, I felt better and went back to work, but then the panic attacks started. Work is very challenging when I get panic attacks out of the blue. I can't breathe and it feels like I'm having heart attack.

Cheryl has been to see a medium and she's excited to share a message she received from Emily.

"She wants me to tell you that there is nothing that we could have done, and she loves us."

Cheryl wants me to go with her to see the medium, but I don't believe in messages from spirits. I've watched the shows and have seen other "performances" and I always find their messages too vague. The things the psychics say could be applied to almost anyone. But Cheryl is persistent and she finally convinces me to go to the medium with her. I don't believe in an afterlife. I think once we die it's the end.

Cheryl and I arrive early and we're sitting in the waiting room. I feel nervous. It is strange to be nervous since I don't believe in the stuff. So why am I feeling nervous? Maybe a part of me is hoping we might get a visitation from you, Em. But I don't believe in it, so…

The medium says that you are happy that I've been spending time with your mom.

Well, that's kind of obvious, I think, given that I'm sitting here with your mom.

Then the medium says, "Emily is sitting by a pond. There are some ducks. Did you two used to go to a special pond?"

Emily and I loved walking in Stanley Park and we often sat by Lost Lagoon to drink our coffees and watch the ducks paddling around. We didn't do that as often after she got sick.

"I see you—or is it you and Emily?—jumping out of a plane. You're skydiving or parachuting," the medium says.

Emily and I had booked skydiving lessons. I chickened out and cancelled, but Emily did it and loved it. She wanted me to do it. "Face your fear, Kayla," Emily would say.

As we sit here, I waver between believing that the medium is really connecting with Emily and that she's just making things up. Where did she get all that about a plane, a parachute, and skydiving?

If I would have said no to parachuting and skydiving, then maybe she would've said that we flew somewhere together. Of course, best friends in their mid-twenties would've flown together at some point. And the same thing with the pond—that's so general. We live in Vancouver where there are loads of walking trails near ponds. But at the same time, I can't help wondering if it really is Emily? Is Em trying to tell me that she's still here?

I've made an appointment to see another medium. But when I booked it, I gave her a fake first and last name. I didn't want her to Google my name or go to my social media accounts and read my posts. And I didn't tell her that I am going to be there to connect with my best friend. I told her that I wanted to connect with my grandmother who recently passed.

Right away, the medium says, "I see a young woman sitting by a pond. She wants you to know that she is sorry for the pain she caused you."

Pond again? I thought.

Em, you're here.

The medium continues, "She is holding a backpack. It seems that you and she either went on a backpacking trip or were planning on going."

Emily and I were going on a backpacking trip to Spain, Portugal, and Morocco. We had been planning it for years, but then Emily got sick.

Cheryl and I have started meeting once a week at the pond. It has become our tradition: coffee and a cookie by the pond. When we order coffee, they write our names on the cups. We always get a cup for Emily. Cheryl and I chuckle when we hear Emily's name being called. On the way to the pond, we hand Emily's coffee and cookie to the first homeless person we run into.

A year has passed, and Cheryl and I are carrying on with our ritual by the pond. On one of our coffee dates Cheryl shows up wearing a big backpack. The coffee shop is too crowded for the backpack so I get our coffees, head to the pond and, enroute, I give Emily's coffee and cookie away.

We've been only a few months into our routine when we asked Emily to come be with us by the pond and help us heal from her loss. I no longer know what I believe. All I know is that I'm hurting and I hope one day I see a sign that Emily is here.

Hi Em! Are you here?

I look at the large backpack that Cheryl brought with her and wonder if she's going on a trip, "Are you going somewhere?" I ask.

She passes it over to me and says, "Please take Em with you. Travelling to Europe with you was her dream, but her illness stole that from her."

Cheryl has sewn a tiny angel out of emerald-green beads on the backpack. A couple of mediums have mentioned seeing an emerald-green light radiating from Emily.

"Here is the money for the airline ticket and all your expenses. I had been saving for her university tuition, but she didn't make it. I hope that I'm not asking too much."

I break into tears and hold the backpack to my chest. My shiny, emerald-green angel.

I kept hoping that, one day, Emily would feel better and we would go on the backpacking trip we had been dreaming about since high school. I kept hoping she would get tired of the lifestyle she'd chosen and make a complete shift. I believed that she had it in her, but I was blind, deaf, and ignorant to her disease.

I didn't know anything about mental illness and that it is a disease, like cancer. Some cancer patients are healed with medications and surgery, or they find their own way of healing.

Others lose their lives. If I had understood her mental illness, I would've stayed by her. We don't abandon our friends who have cancer, but we do leave our loved ones who suffer mental illness because we don't understand the illness. We think it's something that can be controlled by choice.

I've taken a month off work and have chosen to go to Morocco. Alex had wanted to come with me, and a part of me is nervous about travelling solo, but I know this journey is meant for me to take alone with Emily as my companion.

"Em, I'm really counting on you. You're going to be my travel guide in Morocco."

After a few days in Casablanca, I get on a minibus to explore some of the small coastal towns. I have avoided the big cities and opted for places that are not as touristy. I'm keeping my mind and emotions alert for signs that Emily is with me.

A sound makes me jump up in bed. It is someone at the mosque chanting "Allahu Akbar", calling Muslims to sunrise prayer. I have been in Morocco for one week, but the other places I stayed were never this close to a mosque. I am exhausted and I have tried to go back to sleep. I bury my head under the pillow, but I can't drown out the sound.

I have been tired all day. I ask the owner of the place I'm staying, Shamia, if there is somewhere in town where I won't hear the sunrise prayer. She shakes her head, smiles, and tells me, "You will hear it everywhere."

I have planned to stay for a couple more days because the town is so beautiful. I visited the bazaar and walked aimlessly through the streets, listening to people speaking Arabic, French, and so many other languages. I've gone back to the bazaar several times to admire the elegant fabrics and dazzling, intricate rugs. The smell of Moroccan spices and the noise that hovers over everything is so unfamiliar. And yet it feels like I have been here before.

Shamia has suggested I join her downstairs for tea if the sunrise prayer wakes me up again.

This morning… "Allahu Akbar"… and I jump out of bed. I can feel Em laughing and telling me, "Fuck the sleep. Go have tea with Shamia."

I'm laughing out loud. Oh, that was definitely Emily before her illness—an adventurer who loved getting to know people.

Shamia does her sunrise prayer at home. She doesn't go to the mosque.

Okay, I'm going, Em! After all, you sent me here.

When I get downstairs, I can smell the tea, but Shamia is not in the kitchen, she is praying in her room. After tea she sets up the table for breakfast and invites me to join her.

Shamia sleeps on the roof. I ask her if I can sleep on the roof, too. She has mattresses that are similar to futons, but very thin and light. She keeps them in a small room on the roof.

My first night sleeping on the roof under the stars is a wonderful mixture of tranquility and excitement. It's much cooler than my air-conditioned room.

Look, Em, I'm sleeping on a roof.

I know that this is exactly what she would have done. She would've also become best friends with Shamia. That's one thing I can't do—I just don't know how to make small talk with someone I've just met. Emily was an expert at small talk. Shamia speaks broken English and French.

I have surrendered to the sound of "Allahu Akbar" at sunrise!

I've woken up and I'm sitting on the roof watching people of all ages walking out of their homes and going toward the mosque. Why are they doing this every single morning? Don't they like to sleep in?

Is it the fear of being a sinner that pushes them to rise and pray?

Is it rigidity or fluidity?

Is it fear or love?

I've asked Shamia if she thinks it would be okay for me to go to the mosque at sunrise. I know that non-Muslims are not allowed in the mosque, but I'm wondering if we can be in the yard in front of it. I just want to be closer to the people who are going to pray. I don't know why I am being pulled by this.

My body is not well adapted to waking up at sunrise and I generally can't fall asleep until late at night, so I'm taking long naps in the afternoons.

Shamia comes with me. We sit in the yard of the mosque. She feels that the mosque is a sacred place that must welcome everyone—Muslims and non-Muslims. Shamia isn't happy that I am not welcome inside.

She makes bread now that we have returned from the mosque. I help her prepare breakfast for her other guests. I've extended my stay for a few more days. It is wonderful learning to make Moroccan food with Shamia. She has introduced me to some of her friends and we've joined them for meals. When she isn't busy tending to her five rented rooms and cooking, she has become my tour guide showing me parts of her city and her favourite places in the area.

She has introduced me to an elderly man, her friend Youssef. He has begun joining us in the yard of the mosque. He brings us pastries that his wife has made. We sit quietly watching people going into the mosque, and after everyone is inside we watch the crows and pigeons dancing around the pond.

Youssef often wipes tears from his eyes with a white handkerchief that he keeps in the pocket of his trousers. His daughter died five years ago. She was born the same year as me.

One morning, Youssef points at me and says something to Shamia in Arabic. She raises her hand gesturing, "No", and speaks in a loud voice. It seems as though Youssef is insulting her. Perhaps he is not kind after all. But why did he point at me?

Suddenly they both break into laughter. Shamia puts her hand on her heart and starts thanking Youssef.

"Youssef and his wife have invited us for dinner."

"Oh, I thought you guys were fighting. He kept pointing at me. I thought he was asking to marry me or something, and that's why you were getting mad at him and raising your voice."

Shamia bursts out laughing.

She says, "I was refusing his invitation because I did not want to impose. He pointed at you because you remind him of his daughter. He has talked so much about you to his wife that she would love to meet you."

I am so touched that I want to give Youssef a hug, but I don't because I've learned that Muslim men and women don't even shake hands with the opposite gender.

I am nervous about going to Youssef's house. I don't know what to say to his wife and his son Hisham. Shamia has taught me a couple of sentences in Arabic: how to thank them for having me over and how delicious the food is.

Their house is in a poor part of town. We walk through narrow, crowded alleys, where vendors sell everything from food to furniture. The alleys are too narrow for cars. There is only space for push carts, motorcycles, and bicycles.

A young man opens the door—he is Youssef's son Hisham. Youssef and his wife Zineb rush toward the door to welcome us. Zineb kisses me like she's always known me. How kind she is.

They have two rooms: one is used as a kitchen and for storage and the other is their living room where the three of them sleep. Wiping his eyes, Youssef asks me to go look at his daughter's photo that is hanging on the wall. I am crying, too. I know my grieving for Emily is nothing like what Cheryl feels—the loss of her only daughter—but my heart has been broken nevertheless.

Again, I'm broken open and feeling the pain and suffering of these parents who have lost their daughter. I can't resist hugging Youssef and he lets me hold him while his shoulders shake as he cries.

Her name was Salma.

Em, why am I here?

Are you with Salma?

Are you smelling Zineb's cooking?

You took me to all kinds of ethnic restaurants, but we didn't go to any Moroccan ones. Zineb's kitchen is better than any restaurant we've gone to together.

Is there a school for souls, Em?

Is that where you met Salma? And did you two plan for me to be here?

Is this a soul conspiracy? Synchronicity?

Zineb asks me to sit and drink tea while she and Shamia are busy in the kitchen. So I drink my tea and try to make sense of how everything has aligned for me to be here, in this room, with this family who lost their daughter. Youssef and his son have spread a cloth on the floor and they bring food from the kitchen. The room is filled with the magical smell of Moroccan bread, stews, and couscous. We eat with our hands. I cannot hold back my tears—Em would've loved this experience.

I am in the heart of Morocco.

The next morning at sunrise Zineb and Youssef are waiting for us in the yard of the mosque. They have brought us pastries and we eat them while they talk to Shamia. Sometimes Shamia turns around and translates. I don't need to know what they are saying. I just love being around them.

"Zineb is asking if you'll be here next week. It's the anniversary of Salma's death. They prepare food and bring it to their neighbours and to the poor people in the streets. In return, they ask for people to send prayers for Salma's soul. They would love you to attend Salma's anniversary."

I had been planning to leave, but something is keeping me here—something sacred! My original plan was to go to some of the places Emily and I had dreamed about and to spread some of her ashes there. But now, all I know is that I need to be with Shamia and Youssef and Zineb. I want to get up at sunrise and go to the yard of the mosque with them and feel the wave of energy going through me, the wave of love, of letting go, and oneness that I feel as I watch the people heading into the mosque to pray.

I feel that I have known Shamia and Youssef and Zineb for many lifetimes. I have no doubt that Em has guided me here!

I tell them that I will not miss Salma's anniversary—Zineb hugs me and blesses me with prayers.

Zineb and her friends have set up outdoor stoves. They started cooking three days before Salma's anniversary. Shamia and I stop by every day to help. They have given me the easy job of washing and trimming the herbs. By the time I have finished there is a big heap of green herbs and the smell is heart-soothing. I hardly cook at home. Alex does most of the cooking, but now there is no other place I want to be than in this outdoor kitchen.

"I didn't get a chance to cook for my daughter's wedding. As long as I'm alive, I'll cook for her on the day she left us." Zineb stirs the stew, weeping.

I get up at dawn one last time to observe the sunrise prayers.

Shamia and I walk to the mosque in silence and I notice a heavy energy of sadness. In less than a month, Shamia has settled into my heart, right there with my mom and Cheryl, the women of love and courage. Some of the village people have been talking behind her back about her sitting in the yard of the mosque with a non-Muslim, and not going in for prayer. But she has been doing what feels right to her!

Youssef is not here today and we are worried because he hasn't missed a day since I met him.

We sit quietly, respecting the silence of the mosque while the prayer leader, the imam, says a prayer. I hear hurried footsteps and turn and see Zineb. She tells Shamia that she asked Youssef not to come because it is my last day here and she suggested that it would be special if it were just three of us—all women.

After the prayer and now that everyone has left the mosque Zineb and Shamia sit very close to me. Zineb speaks in a quiet voice while Shamia translates.

"Salma's cause of death has been kept secret, but Zineb's wish is for the world to know why her angelic daughter died. Salma's death was not an accident, she committed suicide!"

My hand goes to my heart and I'm gasping for air. I haven't had a panic attack since I've been in Morocco. Zineb caresses my back and lets her tears pour out at the same time. Shamia has brought me water.

Shamia has told Zineb not to say any more because it reminds me too much of Emily's death. I talked about Em with Shima. Zineb is apologetic, but once my breathing has calmed down, I take Zineb's hand and kiss it while looking at her grief-stricken eyes.

Salma, her smart, beautiful daughter, fell in love with a young man. He asked for her hand in marriage. They were going to get married, but he suddenly disappeared. The rumour was that he met a tourist from England and the woman wanted to marry him and take him to her country. Salma was heartbroken after his disappearance. But the tragedy started when she found out she was pregnant. Salma told Zineb and Shamia.

"Salma was like a daughter I never had," Shamia says as she's holding her head down. She doesn't want me to see her tears.

Zineb and Shamia arranged for Salma to live in Shamia's village with Shamia's aunt. Shamia was sending money to her aunt to take care of Salma. Shamia's aunt was going to ask a friend of hers who was an old widower if he would marry Salma out of mercy, so the baby could have a birth certificate.

Shamia explains about the struggle of unwed mothers and their illegitimate children in Morocco. Children born out of wedlock are "illegal" and the process to "legitimize" a child and get a birth certificate is very difficult—almost impossible—if the father is not present.

Zineb hands me an envelope and leaves. Shamia and I walk back home. Inside the envelope are photographs of Salma as a gorgeous striking young woman. Salma could not bear the idea of giving birth to her child who would be labelled a bastard and killed herself instead.

"I want the world to know of this injustice. Please write her story. There are many young women who face the same adversity and the same injustice my daughter endured."

Zineb asks me not to use Salma's name. "Call her Malak. 'Malak' means angel. No child is a bastard. In the heart of Allah, every child is an angel and my daughter was not a sinner. Youssef does not know of this. He is praying for justice. I'm fighting against injustice."

Zineb tells me she has spent many years blaming herself for everything that led to Salma's suicide and, during those years, she lost the one thing that always healed her wounds: her love of Allah. She was angry at Allah and couldn't reconcile how, in any religion, her grandchild could be an illegal child and her daughter a sinner. She was angry at Allah for creating heaven and hell. The imams always preach of heaven for the righteous and hell for the sinners. Zineb says she often wondered if her daughter and her baby were in hell. If so, then she, Zineb, would become a non-believer and go to hell, too.

"I was angry with the man Salma loved and trusted—the father of her child. Then one night, I dreamed that Salma was holding her baby while sitting on a lush bed of green grass with flowers all around her. I walked toward her and wanted to tell her that, all this time, I thought she was in hell, but no words came out of my mouth.

"Salma said, 'Mother, we've been living here.'

"I woke up that morning and made food and gave it to the poor. Youssef asked me what had happened. I told him, 'Youssef, there is no hell. There's only heaven.'

"I should've known that," Zineb concludes. "I have said this prayer all my life:

"Bismillah al-Rahman al-Rahim. In the Name of Allah, the most Compassionate, the most Forgiving. Why did I believe otherwise?"

Emily, I thought you sent me to Morocco to hear your laughter again. I thought the other side of grief was happiness. But you brought me to the heart of a grieving mother so I could learn how to grieve.

Grieve with no regrets, blame, or guilt—just grieve and feel the pain of physical separation and pray that one day the darkness will lift so I can be united with your light, the light of my loved one. You came to my rescue once again by placing me on healing ground. Now please help me write this. Your mom is doing all the research about the unwed mothers and illegitimate children in Morocco and I'm writing Salma's story with the help of Shamia.

Emily,

I listened with my heart for any whisper coming from you…

I looked with my eyes for any sign coming from you…

I heard you in the sunrise prayer of "Allahu Akbar."

I saw you in the most unusual places—in the yard of the mosque.

Are you trying to make me understand that faith heals?

That there is only one God, the most Compassionate?

And that there is only one religion—Love?

Now when I sit with your mom on the bench beside the pond

I see you as a bright, emerald-green light sitting with us.

I see you in the presence of another enormous light. I don't know what it is.

Is it God, Goddess, Allah, The Great Spirit?

In the Name of Allah, The Most Compassionate, The Most Forgiving, this is the story of Malak the Angel.

Masturbating in a Buddhist Monastery

STEVE PHONED TO tell me he was coming home for dinner. He's been so busy at work lately, we hardly ever dine together unless it's a work-related dinner party or a meal with friends. I asked Nancy, our live-in housekeeper, to pick up halibut steaks—Steve's favourite. Things haven't been going well between us for years. He's always at work, never home, and we seldom take a vacation. Our sex life sucks. I want more but he's too tired or comes home so late that by that time he gets in I'm sound asleep.

We sat by the pool drinking wine until supper was ready. I was putting a piece of halibut in my mouth when Steve told me that he wanted a divorce. I couldn't make a sound. Not a word came out of my mouth.

"Darling, you might want to put the fork down," he said.

My mouth was frozen open with a piece of fish poised for entry.

The piece of fish fell down from the fork on my plate. It made me jump. Now my hand was in the air with the fork and my mouth was still frozen open. My throat felt dry like sandpaper. It wasn't just my mouth frozen, everything was still and frozen.

Still holding the fork in the air, I asked, "Are you seeing someone?"

"No! I'm just unhappy and I need to be on my own. I've spoken to my lawyer and you will be able to carry on with your lifestyle, but you won't be able to stay in the house." Steve sounded like a recorded voice. Had he memorized what he was going to tell me? "You know that I bought this place with the money I inherited—that's well-documented. So the house is mine," and then he got up and left.

He didn't come home that night. I couldn't sit still. I just walked around and around the house. I don't know how many times I walked around the pool. Nancy kept asking if there was anything I wanted to eat or drink.

"Nancy, has Steve ever brought a woman here? Have you ever heard him talking to a woman on the phone?"

She was as shocked as I was. I asked Steve to tell our kids. I didn't have the strength to tell them myself.

All our friends were our mutual friends. The only person I wanted to talk to was Alex—she and I had stayed close since university. But Alex lived in Toronto and it was midnight there.

I was up all night. I checked our joint bank account and visa statements for any sign of Steve being with someone else, for any hotel bookings or gifts. Anything? Nothing.

I tried to log in to his email account, but none of the passwords that I tried worked. I had opened a Facebook account for him a couple of years ago, but he wasn't interested so there were mainly the photos of our kids that I had tagged him on, but I thought I should check it anyway. His name didn't show up in the search on Facebook.

"Sorry for waking you up, Nancy, but could you please do me a favour?"

"Sure, sure…"

Nancy and Steve were Facebook friends. I asked her to check out Steve's page on Facebook. His name didn't show up on her friends list either. Apparently, he had blocked both of us. I went to our mutual friend's accounts to see if his name would show up, but there was no trace of him on Facebook. He must have blocked me. But he didn't have a clue how to use Facebook, I thought.

"Nancy, he must be seeing someone. It must be the woman who blocked me and she must have blocked you, too, so you wouldn't tell me anything."

"I expected more from Steve," Nancy said.

"I don't need you to do any house chores tomorrow, Nancy, just please cancel all my appointments for the next week. Except with Chantel. Why don't you pour a glass of wine for yourself, now that you are totally awake?"

We drank wine and I talked non-stop all night. She slept on the sofa in the living room, listening to me rattle on all night.

I couldn't go to our bedroom, so I sat in the living room watching Nancy sleep.

What will happen to Nancy, I wondered? Will I be able to keep her? What did he mean by "maintaining my lifestyle"? My head was aching with thoughts and unanswerable questions and my body was shaking with the thought of Steve being with another woman.

The next morning, I waited until nine, then I phoned Rachel. Her husband was a close friend of Steve's. I asked the question.

"Oh Jen, I'm so sorry… yes… there is another woman. Please forgive me, Tim made me swear I wouldn't tell you. But I knew that if you ever asked me I was going to tell you. Her name is Hanna and she is only twenty-two."

"Gross! Steve is sleeping with a woman the same age as our son Nicholas."

"I know. I feel horrible that I didn't tell you sooner. Ever since I found out I couldn't stop thinking about you and what I would do if Tim ever did that to me."

"Do you know how long it's been going on? "

"Tim said it's been about a year. I found out about two months ago when we ran into Steve and her at a restaurant. I was shocked."

I kept Rachel on the phone for more than an hour. She didn't know much other than when she had seen them at the restaurant and that Tim confirmed that Steve had been seeing her for about a year. Rachel said she had refused to hang out with us as a couple until Steve told me about Hanna.

Rachel came over the next morning and drove me to my doctor to get a prescription for sleeping pills. He also prescribed an antidepressant. The following two months were a fog. I cried and talked about Steve and his mistress. Mom and Dad helped me pick out a condo. I cried the whole time. Mom and Dad had to talk to the realtor. I just couldn't care. I loved my house and I didn't want to move. It was a sad day when I left the house and said goodbye to Nancy. Steve let her go and I couldn't afford her.

After Steve left many of our mutual friends hung out with him and his mistress. The wives called to ask me for lunch and I continued seeing them because I had no other friends. But it felt fake and awkward, except with Rachel.

Before long, friends lost interest in hearing me talk about Steve.

"Jen, I understand what you're going through. I hope you can put Steve behind you and move on. I hope you'll meet a nice man. You deserve someone who treats you well."

I couldn't believe that after only six months they were talking about me dating someone else. Steve and I had been together for twenty-four years. I was already planning our twenty-fifth anniversary.

I didn't just lose Steve; I lost *we, us, ours*. I was the one who could easily start a conversation with people I met at the gym or at the yoga studio, but now I had to be wary of not using we, us, ours because it would open the door to a conversation I didn't want to have: explaining what happened to us.

"Our condo in Hawaii, oops, my condo in Hawaii…"

How… when… have I lost me?

The only person who never got tired of me talking about how I'm hurting is my manicurist, Chantel. She wants to know all the details; how young is Steve's mistress?

"No way, Nicholas's age?" Chantel says with her face showing disgust.

And the latest news is that she has officially moved into our house. Oh, wait a second—*his* house, and now it's *their* house.

"If that bitch comes here, I'm gonna tell her off and then I'll kick her out. I know she's just a kid, but she ruined a family. And let's not talk about Steve or I will lose it. How dare he hurt you like this and sleep with someone the same age as his son."

Chantel is the friend, therapist, and a cheerleader that I needed at this time of my life.

I only stayed away from my gym for a couple of weeks. I love going to the gym. I used to go to yoga classes for athletes, but then someone recommended I try Rebecca's class. She was offering gentle yoga and meditation. I was told that the meditation would help with my racing thoughts. Sometimes at the end of class when we are lying down in Shavasana and Rebecca does guided meditation the tears run down my face and onto my yoga mat.

I loved Steve. The person I didn't love was me.

Somewhere in loving him I lost myself.

I just followed the other rich wives, shopped at the stores where they shopped, went to the gym they went to, hired the trainer they hired, copied their style of furniture and used the piano teacher they used for my Nicholas and Megan. I thought Steve was proud of me and of how well I had adapted to his rich lifestyle. My parents both worked, and they did well financially, but they were never rich like Steve's parents. When I met Steve at university, I was the cute, sexy, athletic young chick and Steve was the rich boy jock. My Hollywood dream came true when he proposed.

My head's rewind and play buttons are on all the time reviewing the things that I should've done differently... blaming myself for everything.

A few years back, Steve said, "Felicity's boob job looks really good. You should get one, too."

Felicity and her husband were our friends.

"Are you telling me that something is wrong with my boobs? I breastfed our kids and I'm in my mid-forties and everyone compliments me on my body except you."

"Oh Jen, you're so sensitive. I was just joking."

Would he have stayed if I'd gotten a boob job?

Yesterday, when Megan called and told me that she and Nicholas were going on a holiday with Steve, I couldn't help asking if his mistress was going, too. I pretended on the phone that I was happy for them, but I cried as soon as I hung up. I wanted my kids to be at my side and never ever see that bitch. After crying all day, I made an appointment with my therapist. I needed help!

I also went to do my nails with Chantel.

"I love your kids, Jen, and I've known them since they were little, but I agree with you. They should've banned that bitch from their lives. I wonder how they feel about going on a vacation with her. I hear you, Jen. It feels like they betrayed you. I bet they will really miss you though and I'm sure they're hurting, too."

Hmmm... I'd never thought of Meg and Nicholas being hurt from our divorce. They seem so happy: partying, dating, hanging out with their friends. I'd been so laser-focused on my loss, my grieving... What a selfish bitch I've become.

Stop... Stop blaming yourself. You know that you're good at that so stop it now... Blaming yourself doesn't help anyone... Hmmm, I'm hearing voices.

"Sweetheart, I hope I didn't upset you," Chantel's voice stopped my train of thought.

Two years have gone by and I still can't adjust to life without Steve.

I called my mom on the phone. "Mom, I hate living in the condo."

"Oh hon, your condo is two thousand square feet in a desirable neighbourhood in beautiful Vancouver. Our place is less than half the size of yours and we couldn't afford even the smallest condo in your neighbourhood.

"You're only a two-minute walk from the ocean. Everyone drives to be there on the weekend so they can go for a walk or a bike ride along the seawall. Darling, it's not the condo that you're uncomfortable with. It's your life without Steve. And he's not coming back."

"Mom, I know you're getting tired of hearing me talk about how terrible my life is, but he left me for another woman. It's still really painful."

"I know, honey, Steve stopped loving you. But Nick and Meg have never stopped loving you. Be present for them."

It hurt to hear that from my mom! Then she said, "Don't you think it's time for you to date someone? It will help you get over Steve. You know that Elaine's daughter, Haley, is now seeing a man she met online. Elaine said that they met through friends, but when I was visiting Elaine, Haley and her new man dropped by and Haley told me that they met online.

"I think Elaine was embarrassed that they met that way. I have heard some horrible stories about online dating perverts, but this guy seemed very nice and well-educated with a good job. Maybe you should try online dating."

"I'm forty-nine, Mom. Look at Steve, he's my age and dating a twenty-two-year-old woman. The men who would go for me would be sixty and up."

"Not Haley's new man. He seemed to be around her age, maybe even younger than Haley. And he's handsome and in very good shape."

When I told Chantel about my mom encouraging me to try online dating, she laughed so hard.

"Oh, my goodness, your Mom is so funny. I can just picture her going viral if she shares things like this online: Granny Advice on Online Dating."

There was a poster at my yoga studio about an upcoming presentation by a Buddhist monk called "Meditation on Grief." I was hoping to convince a couple of friends to come with me, but everyone had an excuse. I guess I'm the only one who's grieving so I went alone.

The monk's name was Ajahn Sahn and he was the head monk at a monastery on Vancouver Island. What resonated most with me from his talk was that we must give ourselves permission to grieve and that many people choose not to grieve, but instead numb their grief and suffering with drugs, alcohol, sex, food, and work.

"Grieving is like walking into a dark cloud where the sun is totally covered," he said, "But have no fear... walk slowly... sit in this cloud without judging it. Once this cloud passes, there will be sunshine."

He asked us to question the story we tell ourselves about our grief: which part of it is about our heart feeling the hurt of the loss and which part is about our ego?

Hmmm... If I'm grieving over the loss of Steve, which part of the story is about my heart being broken?

And which part of the story is about my ego?

The story is being repeated in my mind and is preventing me from moving, so it's definitely my ego:

I still hate that he cheated on me.

He left me for another woman and she's so young and beautiful. How about if she were older, would it still hurt as much?

He made me feel that I am not good enough. Is this true? Did he or I feel that I am not good enough?

My ego will keep me stuck under the dark cloud and I'll continue blaming myself for him leaving and for making myself believe that I am not enough.

I'm choosing not to be stuck... I'm going to stop repeating the same story... Fuck ego!

The next day, I register online for a ten-day silent retreat at Ajahn Sahn's monastery, just a ferry ride away and I don't even ask a friend to join me. I want to be done with the ego part of my story. The retreat can't come soon enough, but I have to wait two months.

I go to Rebecca's yoga classes four times a week to prepare myself for the retreat. I love her guided meditation. It helps identify the repeated negative thoughts that come from my ego.

Rebecca's classes did *not* prepare me for waking up at five-thirty in the morning or the tiny bed or the hard mattress or the shared bathroom that reminded me of the showers at my university dorm. I felt hungry all the time. We only had fifteen minutes for breakfast and lunch. The meals were vegan. Dinner was just bread, biscuits, and tea. I had never pooped so many times in a day in my life.

After the first day, my body and mind were screaming. My muscles were so achy from sitting for so long. We did have a walking meditation, but we sat on the floor the rest of the day. After a couple of days, I noticed that some people chose to sit leaning on the wall, so I did the same thing. Ah, it felt so good to have my back supported. I thought meditating for so many hours a day without talking to anyone would be relaxing. *Not*!

The only thing that I looked forward to was the twice-daily dharma talks with Ajahn Sahn. I couldn't stop thinking about leaving and that the retreat was a bad idea. This was for people who had a daily meditation practice already. My mind wouldn't shut up. It kept bringing my attention to my aching body and my upset stomach. The vegan foods made me feel so bloated. I thought, "Here I am torturing myself while Steve is having the time of his life." But every time I got close to packing up and leaving, I thought I would stay for one more day of dharma talks.

Everyone else looked serene and calm, or at least that's what I thought. During walking meditation we were supposed to keep our gaze downward, but I looked all around and at the other retreatants who passed me and none of them were looking at me. Then I saw a woman smiling at me. I waved carefully hoping no one else would see except her. The next day we sat next to each other at the morning meditation. Before leaving the room, she put a paper in my hand that said, "Meet me in the bathroom after walking meditation."

We stood in front of the sinks acting as if we were going to wash our hands, just in case someone walked in and caught us talking.

"Are you going crazy, too?" she whispered. "I'm Carly."

I introduced myself.

"I had no idea what I was getting myself into. I thought this would help me relax and lower the stress that I have as a single mom working a full-time job," she said.

She paused and looked around. We heard footsteps so we thought someone was walking in. But when no one came in the bathroom Carly continued: "Look, if someone walks in and we have to stop our conversation, come meet me in my room at bedtime."

"But how can we talk? People can hear us. I hear the person next door to me farting and snoring."

"Yeah, me too. I must be on the other side of that room, unless everyone farts and snores in this place!"

Someone walked into the bathroom just then so our conversation was interrupted but Carly told me where her room was and it wasn't the room next to my neighbour. We'd been told to bring a flashlight to use after the lights were turned off at nine-thirty and I used it to light the pitch-black hallway to find Carly's room. Every night for the rest of our stay we got together at bedtime and talked for hours. But we met in my room because one side of it was an outside wall. When my next-door neighbour started snoring, we started talking.

I stopped thinking of going back home.

Over the two years since Steve left, the only things I had looked forward to were my weekly manicures with Chantel and my visits with Nicholas and Megan. The kids had decided to stay with Steve during their summer breaks and Christmas holidays. They had their bedrooms there and their friends. It made me so sad, but I knew it was the best for them.

Now, I look forward to absorbing Ajahn Sahn's talks each day and to meeting Carly every night.

Life hadn't felt this good for so long. And the hour-long meditation was getting much easier, although I did snooze a lot. I've never heard of any meditation teacher talking about how relaxing it is to fall asleep during meditation. They really should promote that, ha, well, we are not supposed to fall sleep but I can't help it. There is a part where I sense that I'm meditating while I'm resisting falling sleep. It's blissful.

Carly and I would stay up late and then catch up on our sleep during meditation.

"Carly girl, you are so funny! I can't remember the last time I laughed like this."

"Well… I was the fat girl in high school, so I learned to make fun of myself and the other fat people so the cool kids would like me. The mean girls liked my jokes, so they didn't ignore me like they did the other fat kids.

"I suppose my jokes made me safe enough that they pitied me instead of being disgusted by me. But those girls never invited me to their girls' nights—the boys did, though. The boys would say, 'Carly, you're just like one of the boys.'

"That sounds kind of pathetic now, but it got me through high school. It's kind of amazing how we will bend ourselves for the approval of other people. Survival. You know I learned from those days that boys really like to goof off and laugh, while girls like drama talks and especially talking mean about the other girls. They should bring Ajahn Sahn to schools for dharma talks. Then maybe there would be less *drama* talk."

While Carly was talking, it dawned on me that I was one of those mean girls at school. My friends and I were all around the same size. Some of us had smaller boobs or bigger, but we could share our clothes. And our parents were financially well off.

I never had a friend like Carly.

Then during university, I met Steve. He worked for his dad's company and, later, he ran it. I had a fairy-tale wedding, but soon after the wedding, I felt depressed. I always had money so why was I always sad and depressed? Not enough to go on antidepressants, but enough that I was faking happiness. I always needed to have something planned, like a vacation in Hawaii or an elaborate birthday party for one of the kids or buying a new car or renovating our house or decorating our condo in Hawaii or buying a bigger condo. I counted the days to go to Hawaii because of the sun and the ocean, but if our friends were not there I got bored after a couple of days. Yes, bored in Hawaii!

I did everything to stay busy: the gym, yoga, entertaining friends, taking my kids to their activities. But, somehow, no matter how full my calendar was I still felt empty.

The only times I didn't feel the emptiness was when my kids were young and I tucked them in bed and read them stories at night. They would snuggle right up against me and listen till the end, then beg me to read some more. They didn't want our bedtime reading to end and neither did I. I had the big flashy diamond on my hand and it didn't feel as precious as sitting on my kids' bed and reading them stories and rubbing their backs.

Many evenings Steve and I had dinner obligations because of his work. Ah, I can gag now thinking about those dinners—the men talking about business and us women talking about our next holiday plans.

"I can't listen to Ajahn Sahn when he gives his dharma talk. Do you notice how he moves his fingers? It's kinda hot and sexy?"

I laughed so hard that I pushed the pillow to my mouth so I wouldn't wake up the snorer in the next room.

"Ha, yeah. I like his hand gestures when he talks, but I hadn't noticed his fingers."

"Oh, I thought every woman in this monastery is obsessed with his fingers."

"You know that he was a guitar player in a famous band in New York," I said. "He did it all—sex, drugs, alcohol—before he became a monk."

"Nah? I didn't know that. I came to a silent retreat to silence my mind and detach myself from desires and all I'm doing is desiring Ajahn Sahn's fingers on my pussy."

I was laughing so hard that my belly was hurting.

"Shhhh, you're going to wake everyone up," Carly said.

After using my pillow to muffle my laughter I said, "You're so horny! When was the last time you had sex?"

"Years! It didn't feel safe to get involved with anyone after my divorce."

"Well, clearly, you're feeling safe here. Ajahn Sahn has cleared the block in your second chakra and now it's wide open."

"What the fuck are you talking about? He's a plumber, too?"

I buried my face into the pillow again and laughed. Now I couldn't stop laughing.

I was laughing so hard that I couldn't talk with a straight face, explaining to Carly about the second chakra.

Rebecca had worked on our chakras at yoga class—now at least I knew enough about chakras to know that the second chakra is the centre of feeling, emotion, pleasure, sensuality, intimacy, and connection.

At the next dharma talk, when I glanced at Carly with her eyes closed I exploded with laughter and couldn't stop, so I pretended that I was coughing and left the talk. Later, the two of us cracked up when she found out that I wasn't coughing, but laughing hysterically knowing that she had her eyes closed because she was avoiding looking at Ajahn Sahn's fingers.

"I was going crazy. I can't even remember how many times I masturbated thinking of his fingers. So today I decided to keep my eyes closed."

"What about the other guys here? Anyone else make you that horny?"

"Nope. Just Ajahn Sahn's fingers."

On the last day of the retreat, I did not want to leave. Carly had been dropped off at the monastery by a friend and I offered to drive her back. She lived in a suburb of Vancouver. First, we stopped at a local coffee shop: ah, the smell of roasted coffee beans. We only had tea at the retreat.

We both felt apprehensive about going back to our lives, me to my soulless condo and Carly to her stressful job and her teenage kids. I have always found the ferry ride from Vancouver Island to the mainland peaceful, but now it was overwhelming with the sounds of the ferry and of passengers talking. Carly and I were not talking much—not like our night talks at the retreat. The highway traffic was unreal, but at the same time I felt no rush or frustration being stuck in it.

After dropping Carly off I parked the car and sobbed. I wasn't sad. It was an overwhelming feeling of gratitude that brought me to tears. I felt so grateful that I had the chance in this lifetime to meet a true friend, soul to soul. Who would have thought that my soul-friend would be the fat girl from high school?

Carly and I agreed not to call or text for a week. It would give us time to reflect and get back to our daily lives.

As soon as the week was over, I texted Carly: "Missing you so much! I'm so glad our one-week restriction is over. Big news—I'm giving away most of my clothing, shoes, and purses. I want you to look through them and pick out anything you might like before I give them away."

When Ajahn Sahn talked about needing less it really clicked with me. After Steve left me I had enough capital to buy a luxury condo in Vancouver near Stanley Park and enough monthly income to maintain my upscale lifestyle. Plus, I still owned half the condo in Hawaii, but I didn't feel good about going there, knowing Steve had been there with Hanna. I'm no longer calling her his mistress. I couldn't bear seeing her stuff in there.

But even though I had all of that I still felt I didn't have enough because my friends were living so luxuriously. I saw myself as less than them. I had so much, and I still felt so miserable!

Ajahn Sahn taught us that the idea of needing less brings emotional freedom. He explained that many people give away what they don't use anymore then put a check mark on their list for giving to charity.

"If you want to experience the bliss," he said, "then give away something that you really like and still use, as long as it's not a necessity. Observe how you feel. It gives you the best high!"

Yep, Ajahn Sahn had experienced all kinds of highs—coke-high, heroin-high—so when he says it's the best high, I believe it.

Carly came and stayed overnight at my place. The next day we went through my closets and decluttered.

"Wait a second, this purse is worth two months of my rent."

She couldn't help browsing online for the cost of my purses and shoes.

"Are you sure you want to do this? It's not some manic thing that you are going to regret?"

"Nope! I'm practicing detaching myself from material things. Did I suffer from my divorce because I loved Steve? Or did I suffer because I was losing the house and my lifestyle?

"I really lost myself in my attachment to things! I had all this shit and I still felt depressed. Every time I went for lunch with my girlfriends, I felt like I had to have a new purse and new shoes.

"I was addicted to their approval and admiration and that became especially important to me after the divorce. I didn't want them to think that I had less money after the divorce. It was depressing not being able to afford a Louis Vuitton purse as often."

Carly stayed for the weekend, because decluttering my wardrobe took much longer than I thought. I had filled up two walk-in closets in my condo and I still felt there wasn't enough space because my old closet in our house (oops, *his* or rather *their* house) was huge. I left most of my clothing, shoes, and purses boxed up in the storage area at the condo.

Carly insisted we open the boxes and I have one last look before giving them away. But I chose not to. She suggested donating my things to the women's centre that she'd been volunteering at.

She had been physically abused by her ex-husband, but she couldn't leave him because he kept promising that he would change. And she was financially dependent on him. She'd hoped that if she changed her behaviour then he would stop beating her. She blamed herself. But she finally took her kids and asked for help. They lived in a shelter for abused women until she got a job and a monthly government subsidy that allowed her to live with her kids on her own. If the retreat had not been paid for by donation, I would've never met Carly, my soul friend, my soul sister.

I sat on my bed and sobbed. Carly thought I was crying because I was parting with my stuff. I was crying thinking about the money I spent on shoes and purses that I could've spent helping a mom like Carly. No wonder I felt so depressed all those years. There was so much suffering all around me and I chose to focus only on my life with Steve and our kids.

I saw the suffering in parts of the city: homeless people with signs pleading for help; people passed out in parks; mentally ill and addicted people living on the streets in the centre of Canada's most beautiful and wealthy city. But I chose not to feel it. When I shopped downtown for my thousand-dollar shoes and purses there were homeless people sitting outside in the cold. My parents taught me to believe that giving money to the homeless was a waste because they would spend it on alcohol and drugs. How about offering them food? Warm clothes in the winter? Cold water in the summer?

How was I so numb to the suffering of others?

I'm crying because I am finally feeling compassion for others and it makes me sob. When Ajahn Sahn was talking about compassion it wouldn't sink in because I was so tuned into my own suffering. Steve having a mistress for a year before I found out. All my friends having so much more money than me. Looking at the photos on Meg's Facebook page of Steve and Hanna on vacation with my kids. The fact that I couldn't afford to take the kids on luxury vacations anymore.

Carly sat by me and let me cry.

"I could've bought a condo in your neighbourhood for you or another single mom with the money I had spent on this stuff, couldn't I?"

"Yep, you could. But if Ajahn Sahn was here he would say that's a regret and regret is just a thought that traps us in the past."

We needed a truck to pick up all the stuff I was giving away. Carly called a friend of hers who had a truck. I watched the truck pull away with Carly hanging out the window waving at me and sobbed some more. The storage unit was almost empty. The second bedroom walk-in closet was empty and when I walked through it I felt high, the best high I've ever experienced.

I was the perfect example of the old phrase "apples don't fall far from the tree." I had followed my parents' lifestyle and made them proud by being a high achiever in university. I made their values my own. And I adopted Steve's values to be approved by him.

Now I want to be approved by no one but me.

I thank Steve for being a catalyst for my new journey.

I trust in this journey I'll find my soul tribe.

But first may I find my authentic self...

She's Still Here

"OH, NO, IT'S Mom's nursing home calling," says the voice in my head.

Heart racing, my hands shaking, I answer the phone. Please don't let it be another fall.

"Okay… okay… sure, send Mom to emergency. I'll leave right now."

Just like the last time and the time before. I fill up my water bottle, grab an apple, put on some comfy clothes and drive to the emergency ward. Dave asks me if I want him to come. I wish he would just show up. Why does he make it my decision?

My stomach is knotted and my mind is racing with thoughts of Mom being in pain. What if she has multiple broken bones? I just don't want her to suffer anymore. It would've been nice if Dave would just come, but Mom's falls have been happening so often that I've stopped asking. It's just the two of us: Mom and me.

Her face is badly bruised this time. She fell face-down. The paramedics are still beside her. Our roles are reversed now:

whenever I had a bad fall, Mom ran to me and checked my cuts and bruises and reassured me with her calm voice. Now here I am—traumatized by her bruises and by seeing her in so much pain. Yet I'm smiling and telling her she'll be fine.

"Of course," I lie.

I thought for sure that she had broken bones. But I act like a strong daughter, hold her hand and have a small conversation with the paramedics so Mom won't see me panicking. But damn it, this is my mom, and she has terrible falls every two or three months.

I hate seeing her like a little injured bird. Does she pray to her Jesus Christ to take her now? My heart is breaking in a hundred pieces watching her suffer.

Where is her Christ?

Why isn't he taking her?

It's time! She's hurting and I'm breaking.

Mom is calling me from the nursing home.

"Sue, darling, please call the head nurse. I've been sitting on the toilet for almost an hour. The nurse has closed the door, so no one can hear me."

"Did you pull the string hard? Remember last time? You didn't pull it hard enough, so the light wasn't on and the nurses couldn't tell that you rang the bell."

"The light is red. I pulled it. She is just ignoring me. The mean nurse is on."

"Mom, I don't think she would intentionally leave you there. I'll call the manager and call you back right away. I love you, Mom."

I want to say, "I am sorry, Mom, for what you're going through," but I am choking and don't want her to know that I'm crying.

Even though Mom is in a nursing home I feel like she could be neglected if I don't show up as often as I do. I feel so sad for the residents who don't have any advocates.

The place is often understaffed. Meals are served three times a day and I've been told by the management that a snack is offered mid-morning and mid-afternoon. But I've noticed there are only certain staff members who will bring around the cart of snacks and juice.

There is a big bowl of fruit on top of the fridge in the kitchen, but the residents who aren't mobile can't reach them. I make sure that I bring enough snacks for Mom. Her hands are too weak to cut up an apple and she can't bite into it either, so I cut it up for her and leave it beside her.

Supper is served at five. Mom is a night owl and although she is in bed at seven, she doesn't fall asleep until eleven. I'm told that if the residents call and ask for snacks the nurses will bring them. But the nurses are always busy giving essential care, so delivering snacks is not a priority.

Mom was diagnosed with Parkinson's disease twelve years ago. At the time the prognosis was grim, but Mom did well until two years ago when her disease deteriorated and she started losing her balance and falling.

In the past year, she's been losing her voice and now speaks very quietly. Mom thinks she's speaking loudly, but she's not. I bring my face close to hers so I can hear her. She was keeping up with her friends and relatives by phone, but since it is so hard to hear her hardly anyone calls her anymore. Friends and relatives call me to ask me about Mom. I ask them to phone her and just say hello.

She can hear them. She misses them.

"Imagine sitting in a chair in front of a television all day long with only one hour of activity every day," I say to them. "How long and boring the days would be. Phone her, please.

"If you could only see her face when she tells me someone has phoned her. Let her know that you think of her. It's her body that is failing, not her mind. She remembers everyone and she misses people. Call her! She's still here."

"Mom, I'm taking you out to the farmers' market tomorrow. The wheelchair taxi will be there at ten in the morning to pick you up."

"Let me write it down."

Mom cannot hold the phone and write at the same time and it takes her a long time to write.

"You can write it down after I hang up. I called and told a staff at the nursing station, so you don't need to write it down. They will have you all ready. They know exactly what needs to be done."

The next morning, the phone rings. Oh, no—it's from the nursing home. I hope she's okay—it's her big day. I'm taking her to the farmers' market.

"Your mom is anxious and keeps ringing. We got her ready to go in the wheelchair taxi and packed her bag with extra pads and clothes, but she keeps ringing and asking to go to the bathroom. From now on, you'll have to come to get her ready yourself. We are too busy."

Until I got the phone call I was so excited to take Mom around the farmers' market. When winter ends, she starts asking when the market will start. It takes a lot of time and effort to take her out. She can no longer get up and walk to the bathroom so she uses a pad.

Then I have to find a wheelchair-accessible washroom and get her to hold onto something for support, so she can stand up. I wipe her and change her pad. It saves me a lot of time when the wheelchair taxi picks her up at the nursing home and drops her off at wherever we're going.

I want to cry and kick everything in the house. I need help. My useless brother and my selfish sister should come and visit Mom more often and take her out. I can't leave her there doing nothing. I need help!

I've stopped sharing my frustration with Dave. He was an expert at playing devil's advocate, saying things like, "Honey, they are really busy and understaffed."

As if I don't know that.

In a meeting with the nursing home manager I was informed that it's part of their job to get Mom ready and put her in the taxi. He said I wasn't asking too much.

If it were up to Dave, Mom would never be taken out and I wouldn't visit her as often. We would just buy her a nice bouquet of flowers and show up once a month. That might be Dave's way. It's not mine!

When I walk the long hallway toward Mom's room I always hope she's either gone for an activity or she's sitting in her wheelchair. I don't know why this has become so important to me. Maybe it's because I have no control over Mom's disease and her living conditions so this is the only thing I can control.

At least if she is in her wheelchair I can push her out of her room, and if the weather is warm I can take her to the yard where she can see the flowers and the birds. She even enjoys watching the cars driving by—anything that resembles living.

The air inside the nursing home is so still and stagnant. Most of the residents are sitting in wheelchairs and staring into the distance.

Some days, I find Mom in bed because she is in pain or she was too slow getting out of bed when she was supposed to and the nurses were too busy to come back and help her later. Sometimes she's in bed from seven in the evening until two in the afternoon the next day! Poor Mom.

I feel frustrated and drained about the days that she stays in bed all day. I can't get her out of bed myself without a nurse and the use of the lift. Mom and I would be stuck sitting in her room watching TV. We talk but it's hard to have a conversation since I can't hear her. Mom and I feel better on the days I can get her out.

Today is a good day: Mom is sitting in her wheelchair in her room so I take her out.

"Wow, Mom, it's pretty busy today, right?" I say as I push her in her wheelchair in the neighborhood around the nursing home. "So many cars! It's Friday afternoon and people are leaving the city."

"Oh, I forgot it's Friday. Are the girls coming to visit me tomorrow?"

My daughters visit Mom some weekends, but she asks every weekend if they're coming to visit. When she sees her beautiful granddaughters she forgets her suffering. A radiant smile appears and I can see again her once-lovely sculpted face.

Parkinson's and life in the nursing home have stolen my mother's smile.

I don't know what to say to Mom anymore. My life is work, exercise, and Mom.

I bought a special mattress for her bed because she developed an open sore on her back. The new mattress has air pockets to help the sore heal. Dave came with me to help choose one.

"This is good enough," Dave said. The mattresses with air pockets were expensive.

"But it is not as soft as this one," I say.

"Well, that one costs so much more."

I am paying with Mom's money. In my heart I feel that whether she lives another month or another year, I want her to sleep on the most comfortable mattress. Dave is concerned about spending too much—and it isn't even his money. I bought the one that was softer and more expensive, and it is worth it. It feels so comfy.

I have the feeling that if Dave had to make decisions for me when I grow old he wouldn't be willing to spend much money for my comfort.

I'm starting to entertain the idea of consulting a lawyer to change my will. I want my daughters to have the power to make decisions on my behalf. But then I think maybe I shouldn't be making any changes now. I'm too vulnerable.

When Dave's dad went into long-term care we shared the responsibility of visiting him, taking him out, and dealing with any health issues that came up. We were a team. Yeah, I was there. I didn't wait to be asked to be there. I was there!

Dave is not here for me.

I don't visit Mom because I miss her, I go because I just can't bear the idea of leaving her there, knowing that she might be left on the toilet or that she's left for a long time in her soiled pad or that she might be hungry or that she's feeling lonely.

Mom likes it when I video-call friends and family so Mom can see them. I do all the talking with my face right next to hers, so they can see us both. She wants so badly to talk, too, but I can barely hear her, sitting as close as I am. When I take her for walks in her wheelchair she just talks away, and I pretend that I can hear her.

Sometimes, she waves to get my attention. I stop and come around the chair and get close to her face so I can hear her.

"Sue, get your ears checked."

"Why, Mom?"

"Honey, you're going deaf. I keep asking you a question and you're not answering me." She laughs.

She knows I am not going deaf—Mom still has her sense of humour.

"Where would you like to go, Mom?" I am pushing her in her wheelchair. It's too cold outside, so we just go around the hallways and she gives hugs to some of the nurses. She used to not be a touchy-feely person, but now she is hungry for touches and hugs and easily says, "I love you," to her nurses. Except for the few that she feels are mean to her.

One of her nurses, Linda, sings and dances for her. Her favourite nurse, Kathy, who works the night shift, lies down in bed with her on the nights Mom gets anxious.

Mom complains about some of the nurses to me. I usually change the subject and try to talk about something else. It's hard for me to hear every little complaint because I can't change anything, and I feel angry and helpless when I hear that some of the nurses treat her unkindly. I've sent so many emails to the management, but it doesn't really solve the issue because the home is understaffed and they're not going to fire a nurse because she doesn't treat the residents kindly.

The staff that help Mom directly are called care-aids. But I call them nurses because that's what Mom calls them. There is a shortage of care-aids. The pay is not high. They work long hours. It's a very stressful job and they are often overworked. Mom enjoys riding in her wheelchair along the hallways to see her favourite nurses and give them hugs.

She loves to go to the chapel. It's a small, dark room with a crucifix of Christ on the Cross on the wall. The crucifix is lit from below and there are bouquets of artificial flowers around the room and an altar at one end.

Mom sits close to the altar. Most often there is no one else there. Mom raised us Christian. We went to church and Sunday school, but as an adult I lost my faith due to the exclusion of the LGBTQ community and the brutality that the Indigenous children in residential schools endured! And the church remained silent!

I sit behind Mom when she prays and kill time by using my cell—checking texts, emails, and social media posts. Sometimes there are no messages. But I can always count on my friend's daughter—she posts a batch of photos every time she goes out or travels.

I don't leave a comment on each photo. That would be desperate, but I usually "like" the album. I should be honest and hit "like" on every one of her photos. I hope when it's time for her to visit her parents at the old-age home, the technology of the time will give her the boost her photos give me now. I never imagined one day I would be spending so much time in a nursing home but *I ain't leavin' my mom alone here.*

I wish they wouldn't leave the "Soiled Linens" bin in the hallways—the smell is so strong. It does have a lid, but every time they open it the smell drifts out. We pass by the bin before we turn to the chapel and the smell stays in my nostrils.

"Mom, are you done praying? Do you want to go sit in the lobby? They decorated it for Halloween."

The lobby smells better. People come and go and when the front door opens it brings in fresh air. I cover Mom with a blanket so she doesn't get cold.

There is a gentleman who often sits close to the door. He was shy at first, but now he chats with me. "They tell me that Betty is coming home today," he said when we met the first time.

The first few times he talked about Betty, I was happy for him—happy that his wife Betty was coming home from the hospital—until I found him by the front door crying. I got someone on the staff to help him and learned that his wife had passed away years ago. He has dementia and forgets she died. He sits by the door waiting for his Betty.

"Mom, why are you still in bed?"

It is afternoon.

"I came to take you to the store for an afternoon snack." There is a grocery store near the nursing home.

"They came to get me out of bed around eight this morning, but I was too achy then. I asked them to help me up after breakfast, but the nurse said she was too busy."

"So, you ate lunch in bed?"

"Yes. Today is the mean nurse's shift."

"Which mean one?" I said laughingly.

"Ella!"

"Yep, Ella is the mean one. I like her name though. I wonder if her parents ever thought that when Ella grew up she would become a 'mean' Ella?"

Mom is laughing. She's pleased that she and I agree on Ella being mean.

"So, what are you watching?"

"Oh, you can turn it off. There's nothing on TV around this time."

"Maybe we should call Aunt Shelly and see if her granddaughter is home and we could have a video call?"

I just don't know what to do when Mom is in bed. I get her snacks and we talk a little. We used to play cards, but now her hands shake so badly that she can't hold the cards and her neck is so arthritic she can't look down at the table without pain. Calling friends and relatives is our new entertainment.

"Aunt Shelly. It's me, Sue, and my mom—your sister Margaret."

"MARGARET, IS THAT YOU? I CAN'T HEAR YOU."

"AUNT SHELLY, IT'S SUE, MARGARET'S DAUGHTER."

"MARGARET? MARGARET?"

"Mom, your sister Shelly really can't hear anymore."

What's up with this picture? One sister can't hear and the other can't speak loudly enough to be heard. I call Aunt Shelly's granddaughter.

"Hi Clara. Sweetie, I hope you're not busy. We tried talking to your grandma on the phone, but she couldn't hear us. Would you mind going downstairs and getting your grandma so we can have a video call?"

Mom talks and I repeat what she says to Clara, then Clara shouts it to Aunt Shelley. It isn't as easy as it sounds. Aunt Shelley is yelling non-stop on her end while Mom is whispering non-stop on her end. But everyone is so excited that it doesn't seem to matter what is being said.

Words don't matter.

What matters is showing up.

"It's time to let your mom go before she suffers more. She's lost so much blood, she needs another transfusion and she's in pain."

I'm sitting in the tiny room at Mom's doctor's office. We've had this conversation before. I have her power of attorney, but Mom's mind is still working so I refuse to make *that* decision for her.

How could I?

It's her life and I know everyone treats her like she is no longer here. But she *is* still here and she *is* able to make up her *own* mind about ending *her* life.

That's what I have been saying, but I can't this time. Over the past few months Mom has been bleeding internally and the doctors do not recommend investigating it because she is so weak and fragile. They have given her blood transfusions.

Mom refuses to die.

But now when her doctor asks me about exercising my power of attorney and agreeing not to give her any further blood transfusions and letting her die painlessly, through tears I agreed to let her go!

I say, "Sorry."

I'm apologizing for crying in the doctor's office. I don't know why I feel the need to apologize.

Today, I bring Mom her favourite food—lamb souvlaki. I don't have the strength to tell her that I've agreed with the doctors. I don't want to behave differently because I don't want her to suspect anything. My mom is going on her final journey but she doesn't know it. Is this kindness? To spare her the knowledge that she is going?

Ten years ago she would've said, "End my life when I can no longer care for myself physically or mentally."

But now she is holding onto life.

My daughters come and sit with her. This is how Mom would've wanted it: the girls beside her to the end. I can't eat. I drink tea. At night I lie down beside her. When I was little, if I felt scared I asked to sleep with her. I'm not just scared or sad, I feel as though I'm walking in a land filled with dark, thick smoke. Everywhere I look—dark, thick smoke.

Have I entered the *dark night of the soul*?

After two days of morphine injections and no blood transfusions, Mom has stopped opening her eyes and responding.

I have this weird sensation when I'm walking the halls of the nursing home—I feel as though I am somehow shorter. Like I am being compressed. How can this be? Is the weight of my grief pushing me down?

Mom had spoken to the chaplain about sitting with her at the time of her departure and he is coming several times a day now. He reads Mom her favourite prayers and sings "Amazing Grace."

He tells me, "Your mom loved for me to sing 'Amazing Grace' to her in my language."

He speaks Creole. He was born in Haiti, but was adopted and grew up in Canada. Initially I felt a wall between me and him, but slowly I started to look forward to him coming to sit beside Mom. He doesn't speak to me much, but every time he leaves Mom's bed he puts his hand on my shoulder and that gesture makes my tears run over my face onto Mom's hand that I'm holding.

Mom's favourite nurse, Kathy, insists I go home to sleep for the night and she says she will check on Mom every hour and call me if she feels Mom is getting worse. I am worried Mom might open her eyes and I won't be there or that she will take her last breath and I won't be there.

I've been asleep for about an hour when Kathy calls me and asks me to come back.

Mom's breathing is shallower and the nurses feel she could go any time. I lie down on the bed beside her and wrap my arms around her tiny body and sleep with her one last night till she takes her last breath.

I am deep in that black smoke. The grief comes over me like a wave and when it hits, I put my hand on my stomach and bend forward. I feel something solid in my heart that makes me gasp for breath. I have to remind myself to straighten my spine to let air in. When I am alone I sob like a little girl whose Mom has been taken away.

There are times when guilt overwhelms me—for being impatient with Mom, for growing tired of taking care of her, for not doing more, for not bringing more meals, for not taking her out more, for not taking care of her at my home. She would've been so much happier there than staying at nursing home. And for letting her go...

I am walking under the dark summer sky. I gaze up at the bright stars and feel that Mom is now an angel as bright as a star. I begin speaking to her. *Mom, I feel so guilty for agreeing with your doctor to let you go. I know you didn't want to die. Please show me a sign that it was time to end your suffering. I couldn't stand to see you suffer.*

There are patches of clouds, but mostly the sky is dark and clear and scattered with shimmering stars. I pass under an old tree and feel a few raindrops on my face.

Has it started raining? I wonder.

I come out from under the tree and the raindrops stop. There is no sign of rain anywhere. But I felt them hit my face and heard them hitting the leaves of the tree.

Is this a sign from Mom?

Is she still here?

Something smells stagnant, like a stinky pond. It is the smell of my life. I lived for my daughters and, after they were on their own, I cared for my mom. Now there is no pull. It's as though a chip was inserted in me and every minute of my life was programmed: wake up, go to work, eat low-carb foods, exercise, don't miss yoga or you'll turn into a nut case, meditate to stay sane and cohabit with Dave... and don't forget to push the repeat button!

I've decided to volunteer for Doctors Without Borders, MSF. I don't know exactly what skill I have to offer this group, but I know I really love to help. A friend of mine—a pediatrician who works with MSF—has encouraged me to go with her team of plastic surgeons to Peru to treat children born with cleft lips and cleft palates. There are many ways to raise money for this mission and I am busy participating in all the fundraising activities. I've hit the ground running now that we've arrived in Peru: there is so much for me to do.

I try to get a whiff of that stinky smell today, but all I can smell are roses—my life is no longer a stagnant pond.

I think I should write a manual to teach people how to smell their lives. If they're wondering which direction to take, they should have a whiff—if it smells like shit then immediately change direction!

I am working with some of the poorest people on the planet, but I feel they have one precious thing that we don't have in our rich countries—community support. When a child is being treated in the hospital, her aunts and uncles, grandparents, friends, and neighbours all stop by to visit. They bring homemade meals for the child and her parents. The parents aren't worried about their other children—their family is taking care of them. They may not have any money, but they have plenty of love to share.

You would think I would smell shit in a poverty-ridden country, not roses!

The moment I arrive at the airport at home I start smelling something like a rotten egg. How can this be possible? Am I imagining this? Is it my state of emotions? I open the door to the house and find Dave on his laptop. He gets up and gives me a hug and asks how my trip was. I know he's asking more out of obligation than interest.

We have been sleeping in separate bedrooms for years. He sleeps with the TV on and then sometimes in the middle of the night he gets up and turns it off. I need my bedroom to be dark and quiet to fall sleep.

I am grateful that I am in my own bedroom tonight. I spray tangerine essential oil all over my bathroom and bedroom. The smell of tangerine is the smell of sweetness in the heart. The smell of rotten egg is the smell of my broken dreams.

I am fifty-three years old and I don't know what I want to do with the rest of my life. I was a wife, a mom, and a daughter. I kept my calendar full with work and activities, and now... I just want to go under my comforter and cry.

Am I still grieving for my mom?

Am I depressed?

Am I heartbroken?

Am I lost?

I used to follow a map: work, make dinner, drive the girls to their activities, visit my mom, have her over for Sunday dinner.

What map am I using now?

Sometimes at the end of yoga, I just want to stay in Shavasana and sob, but instead I get up and carry on a phoney serene conversation and hold my hands in prayer position, imitating the yoga teacher, and say "Namasté."

So fucking fake!

Namasté means the light within me honours the light within you.

How can I honour anyone's light when I see no light within me?

I should stop saying Namasté.

I should say Stinky Rotten Eggs, because that's really what's inside me! Something is rotting within me.

I guess it is my time to be alone with my rotten-egg smell. I've told Dave that I don't want a divorce, but I need my own space. I'm depressed and I need to be alone.

He thought that I was still grieving for my mom and that I hadn't forgiven him for not being there for me when I needed him. Two years have passed since Mom's gone. I still miss her, but I'm so relieved that she is not suffering anymore.

After the magic moment of the raindrops I felt so loved by Mom that I stopped feeling guilty. I have no doubt that I made my decision purely for love and if she hadn't been so weak and afraid of death it would've been her decision, too.

Dave is angry, but not hurt. It is odd observing the distinction between these two feelings. I've been thinking of separation for a while, but I didn't want to hurt Dave. And now I realize he is not even hurt. We both had fallen out of love.

I've moved to a small condo with lots of windows. That's all I need: light, light, and more light. I'm sleeping on a futon on the floor. I don't want much of anything—just light, space, my alone time, and the smell of tangerine essential oil. I spread my yoga mat on the floor and leave it—no need to roll it up and put it away. I chose my spot for meditation in front of the window with the mountain view. There is so much empty space in my condo. I play music and dance.

A friend has introduced me to the podcasts of Tara Brach, a psychologist and Buddhist teacher. Anytime the smell of rotten eggs comes up I notice my heart contracting and the urge to cry. I listen to Tara's dharma talks and guided meditations. Sometimes her stories make me laugh and sometimes they make me cry, but they never fail to open my heart and get rid of the rotten-egg smell. I'm worried that one day I will finish all her podcasts and be left alone with the stink.

I've been thinking lately about some of the guys I had crushes on when I was in school. University romances. I should look them up on Facebook. Yeah, and what would I say to them? "My life pretty much smells like a rotten egg. I really hope that you are single. Maybe you would like a sniff of what I am smelling?"

Ha!

I finally sent a message to Sean. He was cute back in the day and I had a big crush on him, but I was dating Dave then. Dave was out of town working on his master's project. I remember the night that Sean and I went out for a drink. Sean was into long-distance cycling. We met after he had cycled all day. He only had a few beers and got drunk. He couldn't tolerate alcohol well after his training.

So I offered to drive him to my house and leave his car at the pub. He came up to have a coffee then he was going to walk to his apartment not far from my place. While we were chatting, he passed out on my sofa.

"Damn it, you invited me to your place and I passed out. I blew it—my only chance," he said when he was making breakfast! That was it.

"Hi, Sean ☺," I messaged him.

"Oh wow, something must have gone wrong in your life if you're trying to find me—why would a gorgeous woman like you search for me after so many years?"

I found out that Sean had a stroke while he was doing his PhD in science. The stroke affected his speech and mobility, and he couldn't work.

I can't stop thinking about him. We took so many courses together and he never gave up asking me out. I was convinced that Dave was the right guy for me and I didn't want to screw it up by sleeping with Sean, even though I wanted to. Who would have thought that our lives would end up like this?

I've avoided opening the box that contains Mom's cards and letters. Mom and Dad lived in Toronto, but they made sure to come visit us in Vancouver twice a year at least. It became more frequent when the girls were little—Mom just couldn't stay away from them. She sent me cards and letters until she got into sending emails.

After Dad died, Mom moved to Vancouver. I insisted she move, knowing that her health was failing. I wanted her close so I could help take care of her when she wasn't able to do it herself any longer. She left her friends behind and to this day I feel guilty that I separated her from her friends. I took her out for meals, she came over Sundays for family dinner, I took her shopping, but I couldn't replace her friends and she was lonely for their company.

Mom never told me that it was a mistake to move her to Vancouver, but I felt that it was. The first few years she flew back to Toronto to visit and sometimes her friends came to stay with her. But eventually no one was able to fly for one reason or another and she missed them terribly!

I've lit candles, am playing the chanting music of Deva Premal and holding the box of Mom's cards and letters close to my heart and weeping.

Oh, Mom, are you here? I miss you terribly.

My tears are soaking the envelopes. I open them and read the cards and letters.

Mom loved to travel; going on wine tours was one of her favourite things to do. There were so many postcards of wineries and pictures of vineyards. I get up and open a bottle of wine, but I'm not a wine-drinker like her. She even had a bottle at the old-age home: the nurse who was in charge of the medications kept Mom's wine in her medicine room and would pour a glass for Mom at dinner time. She was allowed only one glass, but when I visited her in the evening I brought a bottle and she drank while I was there. I was not allowed to leave the bottle in her room—that was a rule. They were—and rightly so—afraid Mom might get drunk and fall or that another resident could steal Mom's wine and drink it.

Now as I'm going through her postcards and letters I pour a glass for Mom and place it by her photo. I've poured another glass for me.

Ah, how she cheered up after a glass of wine. Towards the end she had to drink everything from a straw. The Parkinson's made swallowing difficult.

"Darling, I've had enough. I might get drunk and make a pass at Mr. Stewart."

"Ha, Mom, you're funny."

Mr. Stewart had Alzheimer's and since he was in a wheelchair he was in my mom's section of the nursing home—he didn't need to be in the Alzheimer's locked-in unit. He was very handsome, and I liked to tease Mom about him. Every time we were about to pass him Mom made sure her hair was tidy and she straightened the blanket that was on her lap.

I've poured another glass of wine and I'm holding it to Mom's photo. *Mom, thanks for all the laughter.*

I want to declutter. My intention is to read Mom's letters and cards and only keep a few and let go of the rest. Wine is definitely making me feel tipsy and I am feeling Mom's presence so vividly. Then I come upon this card:

Darling Sue,

I miss the girls terribly. I will be coming to stay with you in April. I can't wait to see you and the girls—they are the bright stars in my dark nights. I'm still struggling with the loss of your dad—we had so many dreams for our retirement. I feel that I didn't just lose him, I also lost our dreams. Now I'm working on creating my own dreams—not just coming up with some plans to fill up my life.

Prayers are sustaining me. I no longer believe that when I pray, I pray to the Christians' God and Jesus Christ. When I pray, I allow the collective loving energy to guide me from darkness to light, from fear to love. Jesus represents the love and the light that is in all of us.

As your mother, I am not worried that you sin because you don't go to church or you don't pray. I pray that one day you see your own brilliant light, you sense the love in you. Without tapping into the collective loving energy—inclusive of all beings— we are like boats without rudders. At times of loss and grief, if we are connected to the collective loving energy we can find our way from darkness to light.

May you see the light within you that shines so brightly.

Love you forever, Sue.

Mom

"Hi, Dave."

He is surprised to hear my voice. I have gone back to our house a few times to get my stuff, but I haven't called him or seen him for several months. I did ask him not to contact me because I need my space—time to get the smell of the rotten eggs out of my life.

"I'm looking for the book of prayers that you used to read to me. I'm wondering if we still have it? I think it was called… hmm… *Prayers for Love*?"

He's quiet, so I ask again, "Do we still have it? Or did we give it away?"

"It's on my bedside table, Sue."

I hate when he responds like this. He pauses and then gives me an answer to make me feel stupid. But not this time. This time it makes me cry.

"Are you okay, Sue?"

“I can’t help feeling that by making a choice to not stay with the church I separated myself from love. The church is an organization and I cut my connection to it. But prayers used to sustain me. I allowed the church to take that away from me.”

“Would you like me to bring the book to you now?”

“I would love that, Dave. Thank you!”

Kenzie's Mermaids

COULD IT HAVE been the chlorine in the pool? We should have been eating organic food. I knew about eating whole foods and avoiding processed sugar, but we didn't have time.

Jason and I did a lot of cooking at home, but with both of us working full-time, by Friday night take-out was about all we could handle.

I haven't really slept since we got her diagnosis. Leukemia. My little girl's blood has been invaded by cancer.

The first thing she said was, "Mom, am I going to lose my hair?"

So many questions run through my head and all of them start with *why* and *how* and end with *what if* and *we should have.*

Why her?

Why us?

What did we do wrong?

What could we have done?

Maybe it was the chlorine in the pool? But she loved swimming and her swim club—chlorine was used at the pool to disinfect the water.

I loved watching her swim... my little mermaid.

When we swam together, she loved playing the mermaid game that she made up.

Maybe if we hadn't sunk so much money in this house we would've been able to afford to eat organic like I wanted to.

"Maybe it's the pesticides in our diet that caused the cancer. Jason, we have to start eating organic food."

"But what about all the other kids who eat whatever they want?" he says. "Why aren't they sick? Honey, please stop blaming yourself. You didn't do anything wrong. You loved our daughter unconditionally and did everything you could to try and keep her healthy and happy.

"Every child should be loved as much as you loved Kenzie. The chemo is going to be a long process, honey. We have to hope that it works. Kay, blaming yourself isn't going to help and it's going to wear you out."

Everyone is telling me to be positive, to meditate, and go to a support group, but all I want to do is be with Kenzie. Before chemo she was so fatigued and now after chemo she's even more so. Watching her and not being able to do anything is tearing my heart apart.

And poor little Aiden. I feel so guilty for not spending more time with him. He just started school and I can't take him because I would have to take Kenzie as well and she is too exhausted. Jason takes him on his way to work. I'm taking time off from work.

"I am sorry to tell you this," the oncologist said, "but Kenzie's blood work indicates she is not responding to the chemo as we had hoped. This is a rare form of leukemia. I recommend starting her on a different combination of chemotherapy drugs. It is more promising, but unfortunately, the side effects are quite a bit stronger. She would have to be hospitalized for the first couple of weeks or perhaps longer and be closely monitored."

My mom flew in to help us. Kenzie developed pneumonia. I never experienced severe anxiety until now. My nerves buzz with anxiety when I'm waiting for Kenzie's test results. I feel like vomiting in the doctor's office when he goes over the reports. I always felt sorry for the parents whose children had cancer, but I'd never ever imagined the anxiety they endured.

Jasmine, a nurse Kenzie loves, says: "Have you seen the aquatic centre around the block from here? Kenzie told me you're a swimmer. I'm on day shift for the next four days if you want to take a couple of hours off and go for a swim. I'll check on Kenzie every twenty minutes. She'll be fine. You need a break."

I swim a lap and have to stop. I can't get Kenzie out of my mind and the guilt of being in the pool without her—I wish it were me in the hospital bed and Kenzie in the pool. I dive in the deep end and pretend I'm playing one of our games where we dive in together and look for her mermaid toys on the bottom of the pool. A wave of exhaustion pours through me. All these months of emotional suffering have physically wiped me out, and being in Kenzie's happiest place without her isn't helping.

After, I sit in the sauna and sob. Sweat and tears coat my chest and breasts that nursed her, and down my belly where I carried my girl. It overwhelms me with grief and fear.

"Jasmine said that the pool is really nice. When I feel better, can we go together? Please, Mom?"

I go back to the pool and take pictures for Kenzie. I can't do laps—my body just wants to sink. All I want is to be in the water with Kenzie, playing mermaids.

I dive into the deep end and sit on the bottom until my lungs were depleted of oxygen. And when I ascend there are no thoughts in my head.

For the first time in weeks my mind focuses on just one thing—breathing.

I plunge again and again. Each time, I wait until my lungs empty and my mind exhausts the strangling thoughts of losing Kenzie.

I just want to stay at the hospital with Kenzie. I am afraid that she will slip away and I won't be there. I know Kenzie needs time with her dad, and Jason has suggested staying with Kenzie on Friday and Saturday nights. I feel terrible that I am neglecting Aiden. Mom is worried about me and wants me to take a couple of nights off.

The deep end is calling me. I dive again and hold my breath. I imagine hundreds of tiny mermaids at the bottom of the pool.

I don't want to ascend. I want to stay down there where everything is dark. In that darkness I imagine playing the mermaid game with Kenzie.

"So, here is a photo of the pool."

"Oh, cool. How many laps did you do, Mom?"

"I didn't do laps. I played our mermaid game. Instead of playing with your mermaid toys, I imagined tiny glow-in-the-dark mermaids."

"What colour were the mermaids?"

"Different colours, like a rainbow."

"I wish I could play pretend mermaids with you in the pool."

"Well, we could do it here. It's a pretend game. We can play pretend games anywhere."

"Can you bring me a mermaid wig please? I want to wear it when we play, and when I go to the playroom. Some girls have pretty wigs, but no one has a mermaid wig."

On the days when Kenzie feels better, I wheel her to the playroom to see the other kids. Kenzie loves hanging out with other kids who are going through same thing as her, and meeting the kids' parents helps me. We share our terrible burden. We understand each other's sufferings and fears.

I envy the families who have a faith to go to.

One of the mothers has a prayer rug on the floor of her son's room where she prays. Another wheels her son to the chapel and they pray there together. Another has placed crystals on the windowsill of her daughter's room, along with figures of Buddha, Ganesha, and others that I don't recognize. She calls it her *altar*, where she sits and meditates.

They all seem so peaceful when they pray or meditate; they've surrendered.

How could they surrender to this horrible thing?

Why does God, Jesus, Mohammad, Moses let innocent children die of this terrible disease?

Where is the mercy they preach?

Sarah wanted to come to the hospital. I asked her to text when she got here so I could prepare. I knew I would break down as soon as I saw her and I didn't want to make a scene in front of Kenzie. Sarah has always been my one friend who sees right through me and has been there through all my crashes.

I met her in the hall and the moment we held each other we started bawling.

"Aunt Sarah, do you love mermaids? Mom has made up a pretend mermaid game; do you want to play?"

We did, and Kenzie loved it. Sarah played her role well in spite of breaking inside from seeing Kenzie sick, thin, and without hair.

"Aunt Sarah played a clown mermaid who made all the other mermaids laugh."

I needed Sarah's shoulder to cry on. When she left, she handed me a gift: a gratitude journal.

First I thought, what the fuck? What have I got to be grateful for? That my daughter has cancer and could die any day?

And then I opened it and read her note.

"Don't fake it. Gratitude is not an orgasm!"

I broke out laughing. Sarah used to call me after a few drinks on a girls' night out the "Queen of the Fake Orgasm" because I dated a guy for an entire year and never had any real pleasure with him. I was just getting over a bad breakup when I started dating him and I wasn't into him.

She also wrote: "If you can't think of anything to be grateful for, then write down the things that you are pissed off about and let this be your 'angry-soul journal.'"

She met me crying and left me laughing. That's Sarah. We called each other soul sister. And now I'm pausing and wondering what is the true meaning of soul sister?

Like we are friends for always? We have each other's back?

Is Kenzie my soul daughter?

Then every child is their parents' soul child?

Kenzie is sleeping. I'm watching a psychic medium show Sarah told me about.

Hmmm… she is saying a child's soul chooses their parents. Oh, wow, so Kenzie chose me?

And the soul comes here, this life, for the purpose of evolving.

I'm totally binge-watching her show now. Thankfully, Kenzie is having a long sleep. Often she wakes up with nausea.

Now the psychic medium is talking about soul tribes: "We don't come here alone. We come here with our soul tribe: soulmate, soul sister, soul child… Find your soul tribe. Everyone from your soul tribe helps you evolve in a different way.

"One makes you fall so when you rise, you rise higher.

"One lifts you up with love and empathy."

Oh, the latter one is Sarah.

But if we are here for our soul to evolve, then why do children die?

And do not fucking tell me they go to a better place!

Aiden says, "Mom, I want a mermaid wig, too. Nana said they're just for girls. But I want one."

"There are mermaid wigs for boys, too, honey. I will get you one."

"I want it the same colours as Kenzie's."

"Okay. Come give Mommy a big hug. I miss my boy."

"Can I have a sleepover with you and Kenzie?"

"Tell you what. Dad will be staying on the weekend with Kenzie, and I will come home and stay with you, and you and I will have a movie night and you can sleep in Mommy's bed."

"Can Kenzie come, too?"

Kenzie was so happy when we all walked into her hospital room wearing mermaid wigs. She said she thought we were real mermaids. My mom made wigs for Jason and Aiden and one for herself and one for me.

It dawned on me how grateful I am for my mother. She will be going in the gratitude journal.

Aiden crawled up on the bed with his sister and we took a family selfie with our wigs on. Kenzie called herself a "Mermaid Princess."

"Mom, can we all play the mermaid game now?"

"Sure, honey."

"Okay. You guys all have to close your eyes and listen to Mom tell you how to play the game. Don't open your eyes until Mom tells you."

"Kenzie, why don't you tell us what to do? You are so good at it now."

"Okay, Mom. But will you help, whenever I get stuck?"

"Sure."

"Okay. Get comfortable because this game might take a while. Now, close your eyes and hold your breath and pretend you are diving in a deep, deep ocean. Now pretend you open your eyes under water. Everything is dark except for the tiny shiny mermaids.

"Aiden, you will be a prince and you'll use a laser gun to protect the underwater castle from pirates. When you shoot the pirates in the heart they turn into good guys. As long as we play the game the cancer stays away, and I don't feel pain. It can come back after, but not while we are playing. No one gets killed or sick during the game. But we can't play too long. Mom always wants to play longer, but..."

Kenzie was exhausted by the end of the game, but so happy.

Sarah brought us dinner. And a bottle of wine that we opened after Kenzie fell asleep. Sarah is one of the few people I can talk to and I know that she won't try to fix things with easy answers and platitudes. She just listens.

I try to be grateful for Aiden and Jason and my mom, and for the years that I've had Kenzie in my life, but I just can't get there.

All I feel is this heavy, dark, stagnant energy.

Fear. My fear of losing her is so overwhelming.

The only time I can get a break from this feeling is when I'm in the pool and I dive down and stay underwater until my lungs scream for oxygen.

It's like I have to be deprived of air to make my mind stop spinning with fear.

"Mom, I'm scared of dying."

"Oh, honey, you aren't going to die."

"Haley died. Hannah told me. She said that Haley is now with their grandma in heaven. Will I be living with Grandpa Ken when I die and go to heaven? I just want to live with you and Daddy and Aiden."

"Sweetheart, you will always be with us. Do you hear me… you will always be with us. Do you want to play the mermaid game to make you feel better?"

"No. I'm tired and I don't like the mermaid game anymore."

"How about we make up a new game?"

"NO!"

Kenzie has been in hospice for two days. Sarah came and we sat in the garden beside the pond. I watched Sarah toss small rocks into the water. She does this when she's sad. She goes to the creek near her house and throws rocks into the water and thinks every rock is a piece of her pain.

I pick up a stone and toss it into the pond. "My God, how it hurts."

I toss another. "It's not fair!"

Another. "This sorrow is unbearable."

Another. "I want to die with Kenzie. I can't let my girl go alone. I want to hold her and die with her. Please… please, Universe, God, whoever you are, take me and not Kenzie."

I throw stone after stone. There aren't enough stones in the world to relieve this ache.

"Mom, the new game that you wanted to play the other day, is it short or long?"

"It's really short, honey."

"Okay, then I want to play. What's it called?"

"Heart Field."

"What is a heart field?"

"You will figure it out as we play the game. Hold my hand and close your eyes and imagine that you are in the most beautiful place you have ever been."

"Does it have to be under water?"

"No. It can be any place you love... beach, garden, palace."

"Could it just be in our backyard?"

"Yes, sweetheart. It can be anywhere you wish."

"Okay. I'm in our backyard on my swing."

"Now imagine someone you love is there with you in the backyard. Who do you want to be with you?"

"I want Aiden. Just like before I got sick. He's on the swing and I push it. Oh, and I want Aunt Sarah's dog Yoda there, too."

"What does Yoda like to do?"

"He wants to play catch."

"Okay, play catch with Yoda... Is there anyone else in the backyard?"

"Yes, Daddy is there and you and Grandma and Grandpa Ken and Aunt Sarah. I'm getting tired of pushing Aiden on the swing."

"What would you like to do now?"

"I want to sit beside you, putting my head on your lap on the rocking bench."

"Aw, I love that. Anything else you want to do?"

"No. I want you to rock the bench and sing for me until I fall sleep."

Kenzie closes her eyes and has a nap, not on our backyard rocking bench, but on the hospice bed. When she wakes, she says, "Mom, I don't like the name of this game."

"What would you like to call it then?"

"Playing In Our Backyard."

"Okay, honey, that's a perfect name."

"Mom, when I die, I don't want to go to heaven like Haley. I just want to be in our backyard."

Sarah and I are in the backyard. I needed air and silence. We are having a small gathering on the anniversary of Kenzie's passing. Yoda is sniffing around, looking for his pal Kenzie. Sarah is holding her mala beads.

"Sarah, do you still believe in prayers? You, my mom, and so many other friends prayed for Kenzie, and it didn't work—she suffered so much and she died."

"I pray to lessen suffering—but when I prayed for Kenzie, I did pray for miraculous healing.

"I don't use mala beads just for praying. I use them as my empathy beads. I hold one bead and share my suffering with it and then move on to the next. One heartbreak per bead."

"Are those the same beads you got in Bali?"

"Uh, huh. I've had them for ten years now. Same beads, but different string. The strings can't bear the weight of my sorrow and they rip, so I keep restringing the same beads."

I start laughing.

"I can't believe it. Seriously? Haha, I know why you are laughing, Kay."

Where Sarah used to live before going to Bali, her next-door neighbour was an Italian woman who lived there with her family. Sarah called her Mrs. Maria.

Mrs. Maria liked to sit on her balcony with her rosary beads and pray. She loved Sarah and had her over regularly for big Italian meals. After Sarah came back from Bali, she always wore her mala beads and sometimes held the string in her hand as she was praying. I started calling Sarah "Mrs. Maria."

"You were so mean, Kay, calling me Mrs. Maria. Everyone else was impressed that I was meditating and doing yoga and praying."

"I'm mean? What about you calling me the 'Queen of the Fake Orgasm'!"

"Ha, we really used to tease each other. I would love to feel that silly and happy again. You know my guru in Bali told me that Mrs. Maria was my first spiritual teacher, because when he asked me what my first experiences with spirituality were like, I mentioned how peaceful I felt when I was around her as she was praying."

"Let's go sit on the rocking bench," I say.

"Did I tell you that Mrs. Maria stopped going to church?"

"No. Why? She was so devoted."

"I'm gonna say it the way she said it—'I no go to church because priest called homosexuals sinners. My son's friend Angelo like my son and he no sinner. I watch him when he was little. He was just like a girl. God created Angelo like a girl. Angelo no sinner. So I no go to church. This my church,' she said as she tapped her heart."

"Awww, sweet Mrs. Maria," I say.

My heart is broken. I can't stand not having my daughter here today. Or any other day for the rest of my life. One bead per heartbreak. Just like at the hospice. One stone per pain into the pond.

Sometimes life is just a dark, ugly, mean place and we feel like we are drowning in it.

I'm just trying to come up for air and find light.

I don't know why terrible things happen to innocent children. But I've learned that the only way to see the light is through the darkness. I can't run away—I must dive into it.

I signed up for a mala-making workshop. I plan on making a string of beads with all of Kenzie's favourite colours. I still don't believe in prayers, but I will use it as an empathy mala.

One bead per heartbreak.

Kenzie, I hope you see your mommy. I know you are with me when I sit in silence making our empathy beads. I see your little fingers putting the beads on the needle and dropping them down the string.

I miss you so much, honey.

Who is responsible for taking you from Mommy?

Was it my fault?

Did I fail you?

I failed at my one and only job as a mother—to keep you healthy.

I can no longer see your face as clearly, but I feel you all around me.

I feel you sitting beside me with your head on my lap when I sit on the rocking bench.

I pray now without praying. Everything is so unbearable. Prayers are like a flicker of light in a dark, dark night…

My little girl is now my angel. I pray to Kenzie when I pray.

May Mommy feel you by her forever…

Kenzie, please shine your light into this darkness that is still inside me.

I've been an absent mom for Aiden. Please help Mommy heal so I can be here for your little brother.

Aunt Sarah, Aiden, and I have made rainbow mala beads for the children's hospital. We leave them with your favourite nurse, Jasmine. Jasmine gives them away as presents to the parents of the sick children. I make notes to leave with the malas that tell the parents about the mermaid game and the playing-in-our-backyard game and how to use the empathy mala beads. When they play the mermaid game, each bead becomes a shiny glow-in-the-dark mermaid.

I will love you forever, Kenzie.

As long as I'm living, you'll be Mommy's little girl.

Can we play a game now, Kenzie?

I inhale for a count of four.

I hold my breath for a count of two.

I exhale for a count of eight.

When I do this round of breathing three times, then it's time for me to hear you and see you.

I listen not with my ears, but with my heart, and I see you not with my eyes, but with my soul. If you find me first, then give me a sign, any sign. Let me know that you are ready to play.

I made up a new game.

It's called Kenzie's Here.

Gramma Ji

"AMY! AMY, WHAT'S wrong? Are you okay? What's this bottle?

"Oh no! No! You tried to kill yourself."

Scott was trying to dial 911 and I was trying to snatch the cellphone out of his hand.

"Don't call 911!"

"I'm not letting you die, babe."

He carried me to the car and drove me to the hospital. I held the door shut from the inside and fought him as he tried to get me out the car and carry me to the emergency ward. I kept thinking, "Just tell him. Tell him and save yourself the embarrassment in emergency." But somehow, I didn't.

The nurse called my name immediately. Scott handled the paperwork at the front desk. When the nurse came to get me, I told her that I didn't want my husband to come into the room.

"Please close the door. I don't want my husband to hear a word of this." I waited till she closed the door and then said, "I'm fine. I didn't take any pills. I faked a suicide attempt to scare my husband."

"What?" the nurse said with her eyes bulging out. "Why?"

"I just found out that he met a woman online. We fought, and I told him that I wanted a divorce. Then I decided to do this to scare him shitless. I pretended I was gagging and I was holding an empty medicine bottle. I don't know what I was doing, I didn't think it through and I never imagined myself sitting here telling you this."

"Oh, are you serious? I'm sorry that he's unfaithful, but this…" then she burst out laughing.

I turned and looked through the glass window to see if Scott was seeing any of this. His head was glued to his cellphone. Probably he was texting her, I thought.

"Please don't let my husband know. I'm not crazy. I'm a paralegal at a law firm." I gave her the name of the firm. "If you look online, you'll find it. My photo and bio are on there. I'm respected at work. This was just a spontaneous reaction to punish him. Now it seems so crazy. But somehow it didn't at the time."

The nurse started laughing and couldn't stop, and soon I joined in and we were both laughing. She looked at Scott through the glass and said, "It worked for now, but let's see if it works in the long run."

Now he was holding his head with one hand and holding his cellphone with his other hand and scrolling on his cellphone with his thumb.

She called in another nurse and told her about my pretend suicide. She handed the medicine bottle to the other nurse.

"This is an acid reflux medication. Is this your husband's?"

"Yeah, he has bad acid reflux."

"How many did you take?"

"None, there were only a few in the bottle and I dumped them in the toilet."

"We really can't send you to see the emerge doctor unless you're feeling emotionally unwell."

"Then my husband will find out that I was faking it."

The nurse looked into my eyes, trying not to laugh, and said seriously, "Do you think if we send you back home you may attempt to kill yourself?"

The first nurse just burst out laughing again.

"Yes, no, just..."

"Do you want to be seen by the on-call psychiatrist?"

"No... no. Just let me sit somewhere that my husband can't see me and then I'll go home. I've never had suicidal thoughts. He's not worth it."

The two nurses looked at each other and silently agreed to harbour me in emergency and told Scott, "Sorry, your wife doesn't want you to come in. You can just wait here. We will release her in a couple of hours."

I continued living my life as usual with one exception: I stopped making eye contact with Scott and I stopped speaking to him. On weekdays, I wake up at six in the morning, make Julia breakfast, pack her lunch, and kiss her goodbye. Scott drives her to school. I used to like to ride along with Scott to the bus stop, but now I can't bear being in the car with him, so I walk to the bus stop, catch a bus to the SkyTrain, then take the SkyTrain to work. I get to work at eight-forty-five. I like my job.

After finding out that Scott had been unfaithful—he said he never met the woman and it was only text messages and video chats—something snapped in me. I wasn't angry or jealous. To be honest I had stopped loving Scott a while ago. I don't know when or how it happened. It was just a gradual falling out of love that began long before I found him cheating on me.

We'd been sleeping in different bedrooms because I liked to watch my TV shows in bed until late and Scott had to get up early. I can't remember the last time we had sex—maybe four or five months ago. Julia is only seven and we have a big mortgage, so I'd never thought of leaving him and I'd never thought of Scott as the kind of guy who would fool around. He was shy, when we first met. I could tell that he liked me, but he was too shy to ask me out, so I asked him.

I managed to maintain not looking at or speaking to him for a few months before I told Scott that I was going to stay with Gramma Ji for a week. I've visited Gramma Ji regularly—she lives close to my work.

"Honey, come stay with me for a few days. You need some breathing space," Gramma Ji said on my last visit when I was crying and telling her I didn't know what to do.

"But what about Julia?" I said, "She's so attached to me."

"Julia needs a happy mom. She is old enough to sense what you're going through and it's not pleasant for her, either. Find yourself... Find what brings you joy and happiness so you can pass it on to Julia."

Gramma Ji lives in a government-subsidized building close to English Bay and Stanley Park in Vancouver. Her apartment is on the twenty-third floor with a full view of the ocean.

"When I left your grandpa I was financially destitute. But I was being pulled toward something more precious, even though I didn't know what it was at the time. I found a job and rented a room in a house with two other roommates.

"It was suffocating living with your grandpa and I couldn't stop thinking, 'Is this all there is to life?' I loved my girls, but I didn't love myself! I cooked and cleaned the house and worked part-time as a salesperson and raised my two girls.

"Your grandpa was happy enough. He felt accomplished just by owning a house and a car. On weekends he played his favourite music while he washed and polished his car. He cut the lawn and pulled out weeds—he hated dandelions. He was a good dad and he was proud of his girls.

"So, I left him with everything that he loved, minus me. Your mom and your aunt Elizabeth had already graduated from high school. He died in that house.

"But while we were separated, he transferred the house title to your mom and aunt. We were not divorced yet. The house was in his name, but legally I was entitled to half of the house. I was in India and couldn't afford to get a lawyer, so I let it be. I felt strongly that I am here for a much grander purpose than to cook and clean and work and have sex once a week. So, I continued on my path to find my purpose."

My mom and aunt were disgusted and ashamed that their mom lived in a government-subsidized building. They didn't appreciate and understand Gramma Ji's way of living. Gramma Ji sat on her balcony, drank tea and watched the sunset over the ocean and the mountains and looked content.

Sometimes in the elevator of her building, there were people who were unkempt and smelled bad, but Gramma Ji knew them all and talked to them like they were her dearest friends.

She cooked delicious curry dishes that I could smell the moment the elevator door opened on her floor. She brought food to her neighbours. Although smoking is not allowed, some of her neighbours smoked in their apartments and the smell of the second-hand smoke in the hallway blended with Gramma Ji's curry.

Whenever I entered Gramma Ji's apartment I felt I was in the safest and happiest place in the world.

She smudged her space with incense and decorated it with hanging crystals, a Buddha's statue, and Indian tapestries. I slept on her sofa in the living room for two nights. Then she made me a bed on the floor of her bedroom with a yoga mat and blankets to make it softer.

Gramma Ji had moved into her apartment shortly after I married Scott. My mom asked me not to let Scott know that Gramma Ji was living in a government-subsidized building. I started visiting Gramma Ji for tea after work before catching the SkyTrain home. Some weekends, I came with Julia. Although Mom tried to make me believe that Gramma Ji was wacky, I always felt a special connection to her. My mom had never forgiven Gramma Ji for leaving Grandpa.

Gramma Ji's friends come to visit often. On one of those visits while I was staying with her, I was feeling tired so I went to lie down on her bed. There were two books on her bedside table. One of them was *The Seat of the Soul* by Gary Zukav. I glanced through it and found it boring, but Gramma Ji must have really loved the worn-out-looking book because she had drawn so many red hearts in the margins and written yesses beside so many of the lines. It's about the meeting of soulmates in this lifetime. The other book was *The Essential Rumi*, translated by Coleman Barks. It is a collection of Rumi's poetry. Again, Gramma Ji had red hearts on many of the pages and had folded down the corners of some of the pages. On one of the pages she had drawn hearts at the beginning and at the end of every line. The poem is about when the meeting of lovers is soul to soul their love is for eternity.

Gramma Ji really believed in soulmates.

So, Scott and I are not soulmates?

Gramma Ji had spoken of soulmates with me before she believed that we can have more than one soulmate: "Darling your grandpa was my soulmate. When we started living together we had the same goals and dreams, but gradually we took different paths and I realized that I no longer had the same dreams as when we started. That's when I needed to fly free."

I could feel something inside me was begging to break free. But if I ended my marriage with Scott how would I live on my own with Julia? Most likely I would be living in poverty. I've seen too many struggling single moms and I'm afraid to be one of them.

I continued exploring the stuff on Gramma Ji's bedside table. I was feeling tired but not sleepy and I was going through internet withdrawal because she has no Wi-Fi.

Okay, I thought, now let's see what Gramma Ji keeps in the drawer of her bedside table.

There was a tub of lotion. Gramma Ji made most of her lotions, but this one looked store-bought. "Natural Vaginal Moisturizer—enhancing comfort for intimacy." Yikes! I dropped it on the bed. Gross! Gramma Ji was still having sex? Maybe it's old? I opened it.

It didn't look old, it looked well used. Almost half the tub was gone! I held my breath while closing the lid and hoped Gramma Ji wouldn't notice. Obviously, I had not inherited Gramma Ji's sex drive!

Who's she having sex with? She still talks about John Ji—she really loved him. He was definitely her soulmate. I met him first when she brought him to my wedding celebration. She was living in India at that time. When she RSVP'd to the invitation from India she wrote that she was bringing a date. Mom flipped.

Gramma Ji wore a lovely sari and her date wore a loose, white cotton shirt that hung over his matching white cotton pants. He looked very East Indian, but he was a white American and much younger than Gramma Ji. She introduced him as John Ji.

To this day, I remember Gramma Ji and John Ji dancing at my wedding like whirling dervishes, flapping their arms in the air like flying birds and chasing each other. And Mom and Aunt Elizabeth looked so disgusted watching them dancing a hippy version of chicken dance. Ha!

I think Gramma Ji was smoking a lot of weed in those days. Now she prefers sweet edibles. I tried one of her fudge edibles. After eating it, we went for a stroll to watch the sunset on the beach. That was the most amazing sunset. I felt so free. The tide was out. I took off my sandals and walked barefoot on the wet sand. It felt like I was getting a relaxing sole rub.

How and why did I make myself believe that I loved our big house in the suburbs?

I find it so strange now that I didn't notice over eight years of suburban life that my dream house had become so unappealing and that I had never enjoyed the suburb-living style. There was nothing within walking distance. We drove to every activity and shopped in the big box stores with hundreds of other people. I did walk around our neighbourhood sometimes while Julia rode her bike. No one ever seemed to be outside.

All I saw when I glanced at the homes was the flickering lights of big-screen TVs. Screens so big that I could see in detail from the street what they were watching. And I was one of those people. I stared at the TV screen for hours and I was hooked on watching shows on my laptop. Scott used the TV room to watch his programs and Julia played games on her iPad. Yep, we each had our own corner and our own screens to lose ourselves in.

Sweet Julia living in a big, beautiful house with two bored, unhappy parents.

Have I died and woken up in heaven? After work I didn't have to think about making dinner. Gramma Ji's delicious curry was ready. We shared a bottle of wine, ate dinner, and chatted.

"Gramma Ji, do you eat supper by yourself?"

"Mostly. But sometimes I have a friend or two over."

"What happened to your boyfriend John Ji?"

"Oh, John Ji. Well, after living in India for a few years I felt that I was being called to move back home to teach yoga. He felt that he could no longer live in a materialistic society. He found peace and joy in India and with Indians. So, we parted, knowing that we will always love each other. We are soulmates."

"Why was he called John Ji?"

"John taught yoga and his students called him John Ji. Ji is a Punjabi word of respect and endearment. It has different meanings such as life and soul, depending on how it is intended."

"Hmmm... I never googled what it meant. I thought it means dear or darling. Like my darling Gramma."

"Amy, you're such a sweet, precious soul. You've been always my Amy Ji."

After dinner, Gramma Ji picked up a book to read and I napped. I was physically exhausted. Was I used to this exhaustion?

"Darling," Gramma Ji whispered, "I'm sorry to wake you up, but I'm going for my evening stroll. You told me that you wanted to come."

"Oh, wow, that was a long nap. I've been so tired. Why am I so exhausted?"

What Gramma Ji meant by going for a stroll was that she rode her electric wheelchair and I walked beside her. The streets were teeming with people lining up to get into restaurants. There were so many Asian-speaking people. Gramma Ji pointed at a restaurant and said, "Next time, we'll try this. The best Persian food."

"Oh, I've never had Persian food. Is it hot and spicy like East Indian food?"

"They do have hot and spicy foods, but mainly their foods are not spicy. You definitely must try it. You would love it."

There was a Korean restaurant that was packed.

"Gramma Ji, have you had Korean food? I wonder if it's similar to Chinese food?'

"It's different. You know how Japanese food is different from Chinese—but we label them all as Asian food. The same applies here. My favourite Korean side dish is kimchi—spicy, fermented cabbage with anchovies. It's a bit of an acquired taste, but it's just delicious. This restaurant makes the best kimchi. I come here often with Grant."

Hmm. Grant. Well, that explains the lubricant, I thought.

I packed my things, rolled up my yoga mat bed, and left Gramma Ji's in tears. There was nothing in me that wanted to go back to my life in the big house in the suburbs. Except to be with my little Julia. I had to go back for her. This was the first time that she had been without me for a whole week.

Bye, Gramma Ji. My life, my soul, my respected Gramma.

I felt too tired to make supper after work. All I could manage was to pack a lunch for Julia. I took her for bike rides, did her hair, and once all that was done, I laid in bed and cried. Not even my favourite shows could distract me from this life I had created. I felt like I was watching myself being pulled down into a pool of quicksand and the only thing keeping me from going under was my Julia.

Julia and I stayed at Gramma Ji's for a weekend. Now we used two of Gramma Ji's yoga mats to make our beds. Julia lay in Gramma Ji's bed while Gramma Ji told her bedtime stories and when she fell asleep I carried her to her bed on the floor. Gramma Ji prayed with her mala beads before she slept. She had a lot of pain in her hip. She was on the waiting list for a hip replacement, but she never complained about the pain.

In the morning, we walked to the beach. Julia loved playing in the sand and getting her feet wet. It was a sunny, spring day.

"Gramma Ji, have you noticed that Julia hasn't asked at all about her iPad?"

While Gramma Ji was watching Julia from her wheelchair, I walked across the street and got us wraps from a falafel place. Julia had never eaten falafels before. I thought she could try it, and if she didn't like it then I would get her something she was used to from a fast-food place. She took a few things out of the wrap and ate the rest. She loved the falafels.

In the afternoon, Gramma Ji brought out a box of her beads and showed Julia how to make a chakra mala bracelet and necklace. While Julia was stringing the beads, Gramma Ji told the story of the chakra energy centres. Julia was fascinated hearing that there is light within us and all around us.

"Oh yes, Julia, when babies are born, they can see the light of our auras around us, but then as they grow older most people lose that ability because we don't talk about it. When a child says they see lights around people, most parents say it's just their imagination so, slowly, kids stop paying attention, doubt their own minds and lose their ability to see the light we emit."

"Gramma Ji, I want to see lights. Can I see the light around my mom now?"

"Yes, honey. Take a deep breath... close your eyes... now let all your thoughts go away... breathe again. With your eyes still closed, imagine looking at your mom. Breathe. Can you see her with your eyes closed?"

"No. Everything is dark."

"Okay. Now... what is your favourite thing that your mom does for you?"

"Mmm. Should I open my eyes now?"

"No, keep your eyes closed and think of the thing your mom does for you that you really love."

"I love when she brushes my hair and sings to me."

"Good, keep your eyes closed and imagine your mom is brushing your hair and singing to you. Now when you imagine your mom, do you see a light around her?"

"Yes."

"What colour light do you see?"

"Purple-white."

"Now, open your eyes and look at your mom."

Julia looked at me with a beautiful smile on her face.

"Wow, Gramma Ji, can we play that again? And, one day, will I be able to see the light with my eyes open?"

I left Scott. The big house was sold. My mom was furious, and she blamed Gramma Ji. Mom knew that I caught Scott dating someone online, but she didn't feel that was enough of a reason to "throw away" our marriage.

"Think of Julia!" she pleaded.

I rented a one-bedroom apartment with a den on Main Street. I couldn't afford anything in Gramma Ji's exclusive neighbourhood and this was close enough to work that I could skip the SkyTrain and take a short bus ride.

Gramma Ji took a wheelchair taxi and came on moving day to help. I had no idea that the government offered discounted taxi passes to seniors with disabilities. Gramma Ji and Julia decorated the den as Julia's bedroom. They decided on an East Indian theme. They hung saris as curtains to separate the den from the living room. Julia made a game of going in and out through the draping saris.

I talked to Gramma Ji often about going back to school to become a lawyer. I felt that I could be happier as a lawyer than as a paralegal. I worked at a highly reputable firm where the legal fees were so high that people like me could never afford any of our lawyers. But one of the partners kindly took my divorce case.

The partners all told me that I would make an amazing lawyer, but I felt so much fear. Could I afford to go to law school? And what about Julia? Would I have any time for her? As a lawyer, I could be of service to people. When I imagined making more money and being able to afford a nice condo it made me happy, but what really brought me joy was the idea that I could serve clients that their fees were subsidized by the provincial government's legal aid. Although I wouldn't make as much money from the legal aid cases, I would have the satisfaction of serving those who couldn't otherwise afford a lawyer.

Many reputable lawyers and firms didn't take legal aid cases. I would be an elite lawyer who would take legal aid cases. *Yes!*

"And who knows? You could become a social activist and represent cases for good causes," Gramma Ji said.

"Amy, darling," she continued. "Every morning when you wake up, repeat this: 'I'm open to all possibilities.' Your thoughts of fear will move you away from your true essence, your core. Every morning sit, breathe, bring your attention to your breath. When your thoughts slow down and you can focus on your breath, then repeat this: 'I'm open to all possibilities.'

"Do not let your fear shatter your dream."

Gramma Ji had a fall and broke her hip bone while she was waiting for the hip-replacement surgery. My heart broke seeing her in so much pain. She had just been released from the hospital when she got pneumonia and was sent back. We were told that she didn't have long to live.

I sat by Gramma Ji's bed and read her the mystic poetry of Rumi from her book.

She didn't open her eyes or say anything, but as I read, I felt that she was listening to every word.

Gramma Ji left this world with so much grace. Was it her anticipation of reuniting with John Ji that made her passing so peaceful? She often talked about their uniting again when they died.

Mom called and asked to meet me for lunch and told me not to bring Julia. My relationship with Mom had become cold and tense after I left Scott. She didn't care to spend one-on-one time with me, so this was surprising.

"Amy, your Gramma didn't want you to know about this." Mom handed me a file. Gramma Ji was suing my mom and my aunt Elizabeth. She was representing herself with the help of Grant, a retired lawyer. She claimed that what Grandpa did was illegal—transferring the house to my mom and my aunt without Gramma Ji's consent.

At the time, Gramma Ji was still married to Grandpa. They had been separated for two years, but were not yet divorced. Legally, Gramma Ji was entitled to half of the house. Grandpa transferred the house to my mom and aunt Elizabeth so Gramma Ji wouldn't get a share. Even though the house was under his name, it was purchased while they were married and therefore, she was entitled to half its value.

There was a letter addressed to my mom and Aunt Elizabeth in the file. "At the time, I felt like a bird leaving the cage and all I wanted was my freedom. And I did find it, so I felt rich in my heart and didn't challenge your father. I had never felt that I needed the money from the house until now—now that Amy wants to go back to school to become a lawyer. Margaret and Elizabeth, all I'm asking from you is that you use what should have been my share of the sale of the house to pay for Amy's tuition. Margaret, I am very disappointed in you for refusing to honour my wish. So now I'm left with no choice but to take legal action."

Gramma Ji—or Wacky Gramma, as my mom used to refer to you—you're confusing me. I thought your practice of yoga led you to a world of peace and tranquility. I didn't imagine that you and Grant, who meditated many hours a day, were working together on a lawsuit against your daughters. Did you meet in your favourite Korean restaurant and plan your case? Right on, Gramma Ji!

In silence, I could feel Gramma Ji's presence around me. Her loving energy embraced me. Tears were streaming from my eyes onto my hands folded in my lap.

"Mom, I'm so sorry that your anger held you back from getting to know the true essence of Gramma Ji. Do you remember John Ji, the guy Gramma Ji brought to my wedding? For years you, Dad, and Aunt Elizabeth made fun of him and Gramma Ji. But they were soulmates. Gramma Ji and John Ji shared the same values and were walking on the same path toward loving all beings."

When Gramma Ji was in transition I whispered in her ear that John Ji was waiting to greet her and her face would light up. She often talked about John Ji to me. He got hit by a car in India one day when he was out walking. Grandma Ji asked a friend to send her his ashes in a pendant and, in her will, requested that the pendant be cremated with her.

"Mom, Gramma Ji never stopped loving you!"

Mom was staring down.

"Amy, I will pay for your law school because that was your Gramma's wish. But Elizabeth insists on paying, too, and regrets that we never acknowledged our mom's share of the house. Now she feels it's her legal and moral obligation to pay half. Oh, and we are paying off your student loan as well as any other loan that you incurred up to now for going to university. I'm so sorry that your aunt and I didn't do this while our mom was alive."

Gramma Ji, law school is so stressful. I feel your embrace when I'm exhausted.
Julia says she can see your light with her eyes open.
Mom believes that you've brainwashed Julia, haha.
Well done, Gramma Ji!
All I wish for Julia is that one day she can pass on the light, the love that you have shown her.
Hope you are dancing with John Ji...

Acknowledgments

Thank you, Nina Shoroplova, for the original edit.

Love and appreciation for my soul sister, Cathryn Matthes — your love for *She's Still Here* encouraged me to write it.

To my editors: Gary MacDonald and Trudy Lancelyn: you two are every writer's dream, thank you.

Huge shout out to my publisher, MFC Publications, for believing in the message and the healing power of *She's Still Here*. Thank you!

Gary MacDonald, my soulmate -- I feel a deep gratitude for you walking by my side in this one-precious-life. This was such a long manifestation — what took you so long to show up?! Thank you for everything you've done to get *She's Still Here* out to the world.

Dance me to the end…

About the Author

MEHRNAZ MASSOUDI is an author, speaker, and emotional healing coach with a background in molecular science. She integrates her knowledge of the universe with her knowledge of meditation, using the Emotional Freedom Technique to support people in finding new levels of self-love, courage, and inner tranquility. An immigrant to Canada from Iran during the Iran-Iraq War, Mehrnaz is a cancer survivor, a mother, and the author of two books, including her personal memoir, *Never without Love* (rereleasing Fall 2024), and the short story collection, *She's Still Here*. She lives in Penticton, BC.

Manufactured by Amazon.ca
Bolton, ON